MAXIMUM MATH

by
Kathryn Stout, B.S.Ed., M.Ed.

A Teaching Guide for Grades K - 8
In Accordance with NCTM Standards

A DESIGN-A-STUDY BOOK

Other titles by Kathryn Stout
Comprehensive Composition
Critical Conditioning
Guides to History Plus
The Maya
Natural Speller
Science Scope
Teaching Tips and Techniques

Audiocassettes
A Chronological Unit Approach to History
Developing Attitudes and Habits: What's Important and When
How to Teach Composition
Make It Easy on Yourself
Math That Makes Sense
Strategies for Teaching and Learning Spelling
Teaching English: What's Essential?
Teaching Kids to Think
Teaching Reading, Spelling, & Critical Thinking
Teaching Tips That Really Work

Current listings and prices available from Design-A-Study at
Web Site: http://www.designastudy.com/
E-mail: kathryn@designastudy.com
Phone/Fax: (302) 998-3889
or write to the address below.

Published by Design-A-Study
408 Victoria Avenue
Wilmington, DE 19804-2124

Cover Design by Ted Karwowski and Richard B. Stout
Photograph of author by Karl Richeson

Copyright © 1994 Revised Edition 1999

Printed in the U.S.A.

ISBN 1-891975-04-8

Library of Congress Catalog Card Number: 98-92684

WHAT IS MAXIMUM MATH?

USE THIS GUIDE TO

- Tutor.
- Help children with math homework.
- Teach children how to solve word problems.
- Design a curriculum suited to your students' needs.

USE THE GRADED LISTS OF OBJECTIVES TO

- Target each student's needs.
- Move forward or back, suiting the pace to the student.
- Have the freedom to use a variety of materials.

USE THE RECOMMENDATIONS FOR CHOOSING MATERIALS

- As an aid in selecting tools appropriate for the students.

USE THE TEACHING SUGGESTIONS FOR

- Ideas to help students overcome obstacles to success in math.
- Methods that encourage participation and problem solving.
- Questions to ask that encourage reasoning.
- Explanations of math terms and concepts.
- Patterns and number relationships for your students to discover.
- The learning sequence for specific topics.
- Explanations of algorithms.

THE ACTIVITY IDEAS

- Are adaptable to a variety of ages and situations.
- Suggest ideas for hands-on experiences.
- Provide patterns for word problems allowing you to create more on your own.

Table of Contents

TEACHING MATHEMATICS

KINDERGARTEN - GRADE 2 OBJECTIVES

TEACHING K – 2 OBJECTIVES

GRADES 3 – 4 OBJECTIVES

TEACHING GRADES 3 - 4

GRADES 5 - 6 OBJECTIVES

TEACHING GRADES 5-6

GRADES 7 - 8 OBJECTIVES

TEACHING GRADES 7 - 8

TEACHING MATHEMATICS

KINDERGARTEN THROUGH GRADE EIGHT

THE GOAL The development of students who can think mathematically, and, therefore, solve problems that they are likely to face in their future.

It is not enough to carry out operations with 90% accuracy. If students are to apply what they have learned, they must be taught to reason mathematically and be encouraged to use any of a variety of strategies to find a solution to a problem. Then they must decide if their solution is reasonable—does it make sense? It is this <u>process</u> of learning that prepares them to solve problems they may face without being dependent on someone to tell them how.

HOW TO MEET THAT GOAL

Students may memorize information long enough to pass a test, but unless it was understood it is not likely to be retained. Therefore, math experiences should include the following:

- Experiences with math manipulatives to gain a real understanding of concepts.

- Emphasis on and training in problem solving: making up a problem as well as solving problems given, and experience using a variety of strategies.

- Specific training in mathematical reasoning: inductive, deductive, spatial, and proportional.

- Regular practice in estimation.

- Practice with procedures *(algorithms)* until they become automatic.

- Practice solving problems mentally, using pencil and paper, with a calculator, and with a computer.

Mathematics has its own language, so students must learn to read, write, and translate the signs, symbols, and terms in order to accomplish all of this.

SUPPLIES

Manipulatives to make or purchase:

Counting and place value
Counters
Place value charts
Base ten blocks
Decimal squares

Measurement
Balance scale and weights
Ruler, yard and meter sticks
Tape measure
Thermometers for Fahrenheit, Centigrade
Liquid measure containers

Time
Clock with face and movable hands
Calendar

Money
Real money or realistic play money

Fractions
Fraction bars
Fraction pieces

Probability
Spinners
Number cubes
Coins

Geometry
Attribute blocks, Pattern blocks
Models of solids
Tangram sets
Pentominoes
Geoboard
Tiles
Protractor
Compass
Graph paper, dot paper

A few of the many sources available for manipulatives, workbooks and software are listed below for convenience:

Activity Resources Co., Inc.
P.O. Box 4875
Hayward, CA 94540
Phone: (510) 782-1300
Fax: (510) 782-8172
Email: infor@activityresources.com
Web Site: www.activityresources.com

Creative Publications
5623 West 115th Street
Alsip, IL 60803
Phone: 800-624-0822

Educators Outlet
P.O. Box 397
Timnath, CO 80547
Phone: 800-315-2212
Fax: (970) 224-3822
Email: edout@aol.com
manipulatives, games

Alpha Plus
21040 Scholar Drive
Hagerstown, MD 21721
Phone: (301) 416-8800
Email: Infinity@NFIS.com

Critical Thinking Press & Software
P.O. Box 448
Pacific Grove, CA 93950
Phone: 800-458-4849
Fax: (403) 393-3277
Web Site: www.criticalthinking.com
logic, math reasoning

Key Curriculum Press
1150 65th Street
Emeryville, CA 94608-1109
Phone: 800-995-MATH
Fax: 800-541-2442
Web Site: www.keypress.com

Rainbow Resource Center
8227 Ulah Road
Cambridge, IL 61238
Phone: 800-705-8809 voice mail
Questions: Phone: (309) 937-3385

Summit Learning
P.O. Box 493
Fort Collins, CO 80522
Phone: 800-777-8817

Software:

Cambridge Development Laboratory
86 West Street
Waltham, MA 02154
Phone: 900-637-0047
Fax: (781) 890-2894
Catalog: "Software Shop"

Fas-Track Computer Products
130 Burrer Drive
Dept. C-2
Sunbury, OH 43074
Web Site: www.fastrack.com

Learning Services
P.O. Box 10636
Eugene, OR 97440-2636
Phone: West 800-877-9378
Phone: East 800-877-3278
Web Site: www.learnserv.com

Specialties

ABC School Supply
3312 N. Berkeley Lake Road
P.O. Box 100019
Duluth, GA 30136-9419
early childhood supplies

Sing 'n Learn
2626 Club Meadow
Garland, TX 75043-1102
Phone: 800-460-1973

SRA / McGraw Hill
220 E Danieldale Rd.
DeSoto, TX 75115
Phone: 800-843-8855

J. Weston Walch
321 Valley Street
P.O. Box 658
Portland, ME 04104-0658
Phone: 800-341-6094
Fax: (207) 772-3105

Educational Resources
1550 Executive Drive
P.O. Box 1900
Elgin, IL 60121-1900
Phone: 800-624-2926
Fax: (847) 888-8499

Gamco
P.O. Box 1911
Big Spring, TX 79721-1911
Phone: 800-351-1404
Web Site: www.gamco.com

National School Products
101 East Broadway
Maryville, TN 37804-5751
Phone: 800-251-9124
Fax: 800-289-3960
software and videos

Key Publishers, Inc.
6 Sunwood Lane
Sandy, UT 84092
Phone: (801) 572-1000
memorize math facts using pictures.

Video Tutor Programs
2109 Herbertsville Road
Point Pleasant, NJ 08742
Phone: 800-445-8334

QUESTIONS AND ANSWERS

WHERE DO I BEGIN?

1. Choose an objective.

2. Select manipulatives and related materials that would be the best choice for the age, ability, and learning style of the child.

3. Introduce the objective with manipulatives or illustrations.

4. Find ways to help the child see the usefulness of mastering the objective.

5. Provide practice applying the skill.

6. Once the objective has been mastered, proceed to another objective.*

*If the student seems unable to achieve mastery after you have tried various manipulatives and approaches to help him learn, set it aside for a time. The child may not be ready for that goal, and time to mature may be all that is necessary. Select another objective in a different area in order to provide a change of pace that will provide successful experiences. For example, if the problem was in division, switch to measurement, geometry, or logic problems.

HOW DO I CHOOSE AN OBJECTIVE?

Your long-term goal may be to develop ability in problem solving. A single objective could be learning one strategy: choosing addition or subtraction in a word problem. The objective should be small enough in scope to be mastered in a reasonable amount of time.

It is not necessary to cover or master a topic at any particular grade level. Rather, all topics should be introduced when the child is ready (and here you may try, fail, and put things aside for a while) and then reviewed and practiced until it is eventually mastered with understanding. **Grades are included in this guide to provide a sense of what may be expected at various ages, not to dictate what or when something is taught.**

You are free to choose topics and make up objectives within that topic to suit the child. It is the teacher's nervous expectation that something be completed at a specific time that pushes the child into a frustrating pace. When the focus shifts to understanding and mastery, a child works eagerly, but at his own pace. In each topic *the student should understand the concept, develop ability with the skill (computation, algorithms, estimation) and solve problems that apply the understanding and skill.* Some problems should connect the skill to its usefulness in real life. Older children can also handle problems that are abstract—pure math.

How Do I Choose Materials?

All children should be introduced to a topic with manipulatives, and allowed to use manipulatives during practice (fingers are convenient—forget a past teacher's sour looks).

Some children like the orderliness of workbooks. You can choose a program that provides this approach, extending it by having the child use manipulatives to work out the problems. However, many of these programs concentrate on computation and neglect problem solving, mathematical reasoning, and calculator skills. In that case, select workbooks from other sources to cover these areas as well.

For the child that rebels at the very sight of workbooks, use number cards to illustrate the problem. Set out the cards and have him use manipulatives to solve it and then choose a number card to place in position for the answer. Chalkboards, marker boards, and felt numbers on felt boards can also be used. Look for materials that provide you with ideas that can be carried out with activities and manipulatives. Allow more discussion and the opportunity to tell you the answers. While children must be able to carry out pencil and paper calculations, that can be just a part of the program rather than the primary method used.

In all cases, look for games, interesting activities, and real life situations to provide enjoyable practice and reinforcement of skills. Remember, increasing speed and/or accuracy can be an objective and games can be the materials used.

Whatever materials you choose, do not let them become dictators. Children need practice, but if they solve several problems quickly and accurately, it should not be necessary to complete several practice pages just because they're there. And if the materials include entire lessons that have already been mastered, skip them. Remember, the *materials are your tools* for helping attain a math objective. Completing a workbook should *never* be an objective.

Do I Have to Teach the Different Areas in a Specific Order?

No. Nor should you complete one topic at a time. The information is organized by topic for convenience, not as a sequence to be followed. In fact, it is best to relate topics. For example, use geometric shapes when teaching fractions, introduce decimals after experiences with money problems, and measure areas and perimeters (listed under *Geometry*) during lessons in measurement.

Assign a variety of types of computation problems using numbers taught before teaching larger numbers. For example, rather than doing addition with numbers from single digits all the way to numbers in the thousands, practice addition and subtraction with single-digit numbers. Teach multiplication and division together as well. When factors 7, 8, and 9 are covered in multiplication, they can be used as divisors for division problems. Don't expect children to have addition and subtraction facts or multiplication tables memorized before proceeding to other topics. Simply continue with short practices along with other lessons. Incorporate problem solving—whether word problems, logic worksheets, or mental math puzzles—into every topic.

How Should I Teach?

Rote memorization helps build speed and accuracy, and, therefore, has its place, but it does not equip students with the ability to solve problems. Knowing that two times two is four does not help them choose multiplication when faced with baking enough cookies for a party so that each person has at least four cookies. The following suggestions will encourage the development of mathematical thinking as well as build competency in basic skills.

- **Teach the concept before the procedure.**

    A concept relates to number sense (*there is a specific quantity referred to as five*) or a relationship between numbers (*a pattern*) that has led to a generalization (*numbers can be added in any order and the answer will be the same*). Children need experience with the concept so that they understand the meaning of symbols used in the procedure—combining sets of objects before using the + symbol, for example.

    Procedures (algorithms) are related to specific skills—how to add two numbers, how to divide, and should improve with practice.

- **Use concrete objects to introduce concepts to young children.**

    Older children (10 and older) may only need to look at drawings. If something is not understood with pictures and explanations, however, use objects and experiences no matter what the age.

- **Relate the skills to information that is already understood.**

    When teaching addition, for instance, use only numbers that the student could find quantities for with counters. Word problems assigned should only require operations (+,-, x, ÷) already practiced. If it does not use facts already mastered, a calculator should be made available.

- **Plan lessons that allow students to be actively involved.**

Provide appropriate manipulatives and allow time for students to use them to solve problems. If problems are to be solved physically, be certain that the students have had opportunities with concrete objects before having them use drawings. The concrete objects help them develop an accurate mental image that they can recall while looking at an illustration.

- **Ask leading questions requiring their mental participation and direct them toward the discovery of a generalization (a rule, formula, or fact).**

What if. . . ?   Do you see a pattern?
Will that work every time?   How do you know?
Do you think the answer would be the same if you used these materials?

- **Encourage them to follow through with their ideas: "Find out if you're right."**

It is this practice—guessing, making errors, investigating further—that develops competence in reasoning mathematically. If they hesitate, make it clear that mistakes are a normal part of learning. Some students have such a desire to be right or to please the teacher that they find it difficult to "dig in" until they see everyone else doing so.

- **Lead students to the realization that more than one approach can be used to come to a correct solution.**

They may listen to others explain their procedure, or work in a group, discussing various strategies for solving a problem.

"56 + 32 is 50 + 30, or 80, then 6 plus 2 is 8, so it's 88." Or, "56 is almost 60, so 60 plus 30 is 90. I added 4, that's 2 more than the 2 in 32, so now I count back 2. It's 88."

- **Provide variety in practice activities.**

Include games, mental puzzles, and an assortment of interesting activities that not only give students a chance to use what they have learned, but also give them a chance to know something so well that they can eventually use those skills routinely.

Play: store, games (including board and computer games).
Build models.
Use logic worksheets.
Use objects not just drawings for measurement practice.
Work in a group to collect, record and interpret information.
Make graphs or charts of information.
Include paper and pencil practice and drills.
Include computer software for practice and drills.

- **Help students connect what they have learned with other similar situations, and with the real world. Don't assume they will make the connections on their own.**

Once they discover a formula or generalization in solving a problem, have them use it in other similar problems to determine whether or not it will work every time. Give them word problems related to their interests and experiences: "I have 5 sticks of gum, Jan wants one, how many will I have left?" *Relate math to other subject areas so that they understand its usefulness.*

Business	Checkbook. Mileage and gas allowance. Sales tax. Interest. Expenses/Profits.
Household	Cooking. Buying groceries. Measuring for sewing. Building a playhouse.
Reference Skills	Read and interpret charts: almanac tables, various schedules, timelines.
Science	Experiments involving computation. Problem solving. Measuring.

What About Mastery and Retention?

Mastery means the student can use what he has learned whenever necessary.

- **Provide frequent review.**

  1. Check the student's understanding of concepts

  2. Check speed and accuracy in computation.

  3. Analyze the types of errors made by the student.

  4. Analyze the student's ability to solve problems.

- **Provide a variety of types of review.**

  ❑ **Discussion** Ask questions that help you evaluate understanding.

    – Why do you think that is a good answer?
    – Can you give an example?
    – Can you give a counter example? (What it is not.)
    – How did you arrive at the solution? (Correct faulty reasoning.)
    – What is the rule? (formula? procedure?)

  ❑ **Quizzes** Cover current lessons.

  ❑ **Review tests** Cover past information as well as current lessons.

- **Reteach.**

Determine the cause of an error by observing what the student says, what he does when working with manipulatives, and/or what he writes with paper and pencil. Reteach whatever has been misunderstood. Provide extra practice to strengthen the weak area. If the student still has difficulty, change your approach.

WATCH FOR ERRORS

➜ Memorization of a procedure without understanding the concept.
➜ Faulty reasoning.
➜ Use of an inappropriate strategy to solve the problem.
➜ Inaccurate calculations due to poor computation skills.

POSSIBLE PROBLEMS AND SOLUTIONS

Problem   *The student is stumped from the very beginning.*

Solution 1   Be certain that he understands the vocabulary. Explain the problem in a manner he can understand, defining words he doesn't know.

Solution 2   If he can't visualize the problem, it's all too abstract sounding, have him use manipulatives or make a drawing in order to understand it.

Problem   *The student understands the question, but can go no further.*

Solution 1   The student could be confused because of numbers that are too large, or fairly new to him (fractions, decimals). Have him replace the numbers with simpler numbers, figure out how to solve the problem, and then replace the original numbers and go through the procedure that he found to work.

Solution 2   He may not know which operation to use, or how to compute with the given numbers, because he merely imitated a model to solve practice problems in computation. He needs review of the basic concepts using manipulatives or illustrations.

Problem   *The student eventually figures out how to approach a problem, but slowly.*

Solution   Work with the student individually, asking questions that will help him reason. Sometimes thinking out loud is all it takes.

Problem *The student can figure out what to do but takes a long time to carry out the actual computation.*

Solution 1 Have the student explain his procedure. If he seems uncertain about the concept (place value and borrowing for instance), use manipulatives to develop understanding.

Solution 2 Check for speed in related facts: addition, subtraction, multiplication.
For example: if a student is slow in recalling 6 x 6, he will be slow in solving a larger multiplication problem. In that case, drill facts. Use flashcards and have him keep a record of how long it takes to give the correct answers. Do this daily to keep track of improvement. Use every opportunity to have him practice the facts between recorded drills. Continue with lessons in other areas of math, keeping these drills short and frequent.

Solution 3 First, be certain that the student is following the correct procedure in carrying out the computation. Then, provide repeated practice of the particular type of computation causing trouble. That is, a page of all division, or all multiplication, rather than a mix of problems. By keeping the allotted time short, say 5 to 15 minutes, but having one or two drills each day, the speed should improve without it all becoming too tedious. Let the student keep a record of how many problems he can complete correctly in the allotted time. (Time would be determined by the child's age and ability to attend to the task.) These drills should supplement the regular math program. Don't wait for students to build speed before moving on to other math topics.

Problem *The student has learning disabilities that interfere with his memory.*

Solution Do all of the following:

1. It is especially important to give meaning to the lessons, providing a broader base for the memory. Relate a skill to real life—money to earnings and allowance, averages to sports scores. See suggestions within each topic.

2. Emphasize understanding. For children with learning disabilities this usually requires a hands-on approach. Use objects to count, multiply, divide, and so on. Use the suggestions within topics that help organize the work (write problems on place value charts or graph paper) and reduce paper and pencil work (use chalkboards, markerboards, charts).

3.   Teach and allow the use of a calculator. Have multiplication charts, number lines and other visual aids available for reference. The student can understand and use an algorithm (procedure) even if he hasn't mastered memorization of addition, subtraction, multiplication, and division facts. He can solve a variety of types of problems, including word problems, by reasoning and applying understanding and then using aids (calculator, number charts) for accuracy. Continue to work on drills of these facts, but for short periods, using a small number of problems. Provide frequent review. Drill related facts: the addition and subtraction problems using the same numbers; multiplication and division problems using the same numbers.

4.   Geometry has more appeal and is easier to understand and remember, so shift often from difficult areas to geometry. Keep objectives narrow and shift topics frequently. When returning to a topic, **always begin with review**.

5.   Provide logic workbooks to develop reasoning. *Critical Thinking Press & Software* also has materials to aid development in visual discrimination, which is weak in some students with disabilities. (Refer to *Supplies*, page 13.)

KINDERGARTEN - GRADE 2 OBJECTIVES

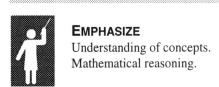

EMPHASIZE
Understanding of concepts.
Mathematical reasoning.

PROVIDE OPPORTUNITIES
For students to use calculators.
For students to use computers.

INVOLVE STUDENTS IN
Hands-on activities to build understanding.
Estimating, making predictions, and checking their ideas.
Discussions to develop both understanding and reasoning.

PROBLEM SOLVING

❏ **Develop problem solving skills.**

- **Locate objects according to position and direction in space, and locate objects according to position and direction in two dimensions.**

above	below	inside	outside	before	after	between
up	down	near	far	left	right	

- **Make comparisons.** *(Use objects and/or pictures.)*
  Comparisons are used in learning number concepts, measuring, and geometry.

same	different	longer	longest	heavier	lighter
smaller	smallest	larger	largest	holds more	holds less
shorter	shortest	taller	tallest	more in a group	less in a group

- **Classify and sort—same kind, color, size, and/or shape.**
  - Decide whether or not something belongs to a set.
  - Look for a pattern to decide why things are members of a set.

- **Identify and use patterns:**
  - Recognize and reproduce a pattern.
  - Identify and continue a pattern. *(What comes next?)*
  - Look for a pattern to make a generalization.

- **Make and check an estimate.**

  Use strategies:
  - Using a reference
  - Chunking
  - Front-end estimation

  Apply to problem solving:
  - Computation
  - Measurement
  - Time
  - Geometry

- **Solve one-step word problems requiring a choice between addition and subtraction.**
  - Understand what the problem is asking: basic number concepts and vocabulary for location, comparisons, classifications and ordering numbers.
  - Decide which information must be used.
  - Make and carry out a plan for solving the problem.

- **Collect and record information in a group.**
  Make, or complete, and interpret bar graphs and charts in a group.

- **Make up a problem when given a situation or mathematical information.**

☐ **Solve problems mentally.**

- **Count on or back.**
  3 + 2 would be counted: "3, 4, 5" rather than "1, 2, 3, 4, 5."

- **Compare and order.**
  Which is greater? Lesser? Arrange from least to greatest.

- **Use patterns.**

- **Use associative and commutative properties.**

- **Use addition and subtraction facts.**

☐ **Use a calculator.**

☐ **Use a computer.**

PROBABILITY AND STATISTICS

☐ **Explore probability.**

☐ **Collect information.**

☐ **Interpret information from: calendar, bar graph, pictograph.**

☐ **Construct a chart or graph.**

UNDERSTANDING NUMBERS 0 – 20

All the activities below should be mastered with a few numbers before introducing larger numbers. For example, begin with 1 to 4 objects to count, compare, order, match to a numeral and add to and take away from. Then introduce zero and 5 - 8. Review 1 - 8, move on to 9 - 12, 12 - 20, and review again. These numbers should be learned without reference to place value. Once a small group of numbers have been learned, move on to another area of math (money, measurement, geometry, fractions, time). Do not use the information listed as a sequence to be followed.

❑ **Learn ordinal numbers through use.**

First, second, third, fourth, fifth, sixth, seventh, eighth, ninth, tenth, eleventh, twelfth.

❑ **Recognize, name, and write numbers 0 – 20.**

- Count by rote to 10.
- Count up to 30 objects.
- Told a number: make or identify a set; identify the numeral; identify zero as none.
- Match a written numeral to a set.
- Find a number on a number line.

❑ **Compare and order numbers 0 – 20.**

- Compare two sets: which has more, fewer.
- Check by matching objects or counting.
- Tell how many more or less (1 or 2 more or less).
- Recognize symbols < (less than), > (greater than), = (equal to).
- Order three or four sets, smallest to largest.
- Order three or four numbers: identify the next number forward, backward, and between.

❑ **Understand addition as <u>adding to</u>.**

- Recognize + as the symbol for adding to.
- Using 0 - 6 objects, count to identify a sum.
- Read and write addition number sentences (numbers 0 - 6).

❑ **Understand subtraction as <u>take away from</u>.**

- Recognize - as the symbol for take away from.
- Using 0 - 6 objects, count to identify the difference.
- Read and write subtraction number sentences (numbers 0 - 6).

UNDERSTANDING NUMBERS 20 - 999

*Proceed with these numbers **after** experiences with money, time, measurement, geometry and fractions. Teach groups of numbers, taking breaks to work in the other areas. Many first grade texts only cover numbers 0 - 100.*

❑ **Recognize, name, and write numbers 20 – 999.**

- Count by rote to 100 and up to 100 objects.
- Count by fives, tens, twos.
- Make or identify a set for a written number, and a spoken number.
- Told a number, identify the numeral.
- Match a numeral to the word *(1 - 10: Grade 1)*.
- Find a number on a number line.
- Identify a number as even or odd.

❑ **Order three or four numbers.**

- Identify the next number forward, backward, and between.

❑ **Compare numbers using place value**
Teach place value after practice ordering, adding, and subtracting with 0 - 12.

- Identify ones and tens in numbers 1 - 50, then in 50 - 99.
- Compare quantities which are less than, more than, and equal to: 0 - 50; 50 - 99.
- Identify ones, tens, hundreds place in numbers 1 - 999. *(Grade 2)*
- Compare sets 0 - 999 as greater than, less than, or equal to. *(Grade 2)*
- Use symbols when comparing sets: <, >, = *(Grade 2)*
- Round numbers through 99 to the nearest ten. *(Grade 2)*

COMPUTATION WITH WHOLE NUMBERS

Continue to teach with small groups of numbers. Have students practice both addition and subtraction, smaller, simpler numbers before moving on to larger numbers. Pair multiplication and division the same way. Allow breaks to work in other areas of math. Formal operations and place value are not usually taught in Kindergarten.

❑ **ADDITION**

- **Learn concepts.**
  - Understand and use the associative property of addition adding three numbers.
  - Understand and use the commutative property of addition.
  - Identify different ways to name a sum.
  - Check addition by adding in reverse order.

- **Solve problems.**
  - Written vertically and horizontally.
  - Missing an addend but giving the sum (2 + ? = 4).
  - Word problems requiring addition, and writing a number sentence.
  - Mentally, using a number line, and by counting on.

- **Use whole numbers.**
  - Zero as an addend.
  - Three single digit numbers with sums through 18, no renaming.
  - Addition facts with sums 0 through 9 *(to be memorized)*.
  - Two numbers, *no renaming*: 1-digit and 2-digit; 2-digit and 2-digit.
  - Two-digit and three-digit; 3-digit and 3-digit; sums less than 1,000. *(Grade 2)*
  - Two numbers *renaming ones*: up to 3-digit added to 2-digit. *(Grade 2)*
  - **Drill** addition of numbers 0 through 10 (both horizontal and vertical problems).

□ **SUBTRACTION**

Subtract numbers used in addition. Check using addition. (a - b = c: c + b = a)

- **Solve problems**
  - Written vertically and horizontally.
  - Differences less than 10, but missing one other number (? – 4 = 6).
  - Word problems requiring subtraction.
  - Mentally, using a number line, and by counting back.

- **Use whole numbers.**
  - Subtract with zero.
  - Subtract two single-digit numbers used in addition, no renaming.
  - Subtract 0 - 20 and a 1-digit number, no renaming.
  - Subtraction facts with differences less than 10 *(to be memorized)*.
  - Subtract without regrouping and only with numbers understood by practice with place value (comparing quantities, reading and writing the numbers).
  - 1-digit from 2-digit number; 2-digit from 2-digit.
  - 2-digit from 3-digit; 3-digit from 3-digit. *(Grade 2)*
  - Begin regrouping tens and ones and practice with simpler numbers than those used for addition without regrouping.
  - **Drill** subtraction problems with numbers 0 - 10 (vertical and horizontal).

□ **MULTIPLICATION** *(may wait to be introduced until grade 2)*

- **Learn the concept** of multiplication as repeated addition using objects or pictures.

- **Solve problems.**
  - Written vertically and horizontally.
  - Using numbers 1 through 5, then 6 - 9, and then review.
  - Word problems using multiplication to solve.
  - Match a written multiplication problem to an illustration.
  - Match a written multiplication problem to an addition problem.

- **Use whole numbers.**
  - Less than ten.
  - Multiply by 2, 3, 4, 5 (the other number should be 1 - 9).

❑ **DIVISION**

Introduce the concept of division as separating a group of objects (or pictures) into several smaller groups.

MONEY

Use money quantities that correspond to whole numbers the children can read. Begin with a few pennies to count and to match to a price.

❑ **Identify value.**

- Identify a coin and its value: penny, nickel, dime
  quarter *(Grade 1)*
  half-dollar *(Grade 2)*
- Compare two coins in value: more than, less than.
- Add groups of pennies up to a total of twenty cents.
- Match coins to a price: work up to thirty cents. *(Match a nickel to a 5¢ item, a dime to 10¢. Don't combine pennies with nickels and dimes for a total.)*
- Find the value of combinations of coins up to 99 cents *(Grade 1)*; up to $2.00.

❑ **Computation**

- Solve money problems using addition, no renaming. *(Grade 1)*
- Solve money problems using subtraction, no renaming. *(Grade 1)*
- Make change up to 25 cents. *(Grade 2)*
- Solve word problems using addition or subtraction with answers less than $10.00. *(Grade 2)*

MEASUREMENT

❑ **Learn the concept of units used for measuring are arbitrary. We have agreed on certain units for convenience.**

❑ **Solve problems: measure length, capacity, and weight with informal units and then with US customary units and metric units.**

❑ **Have students make and check estimates (guesses):**

- **Length** *(Tools for standard units: ruler, yard stick, meter stick.)*
  - Guess which is longer, shorter? Compare to check.
  - Measure length using informal units.
  - Guess length: check by measuring with standard units: inches, feet, yards.
  - Guess and check using metric units: centimeters.
  - Measure perimeter in inches and centimeters.

- **Capacity**
  - Guess which holds more (capacity): compare to check.
  - Compare liquid measures (holds more, less).
  - Check comparison using standard units: cup, pint, quart.
  - Identify number of cups in a pint, pints in a quart.
  - Estimate and check capacity using metric measure: liters.

- **Weight**
  - Guess which of two items is heavier: use a balance scale to check.
  - Check weight using standard unit: pounds.
  - Check weight using standard metric units: kilograms.

- **Temperature**
  - Recognize temperature as hot, cold (hotter, hottest, colder, coldest).
  - Identify red line on a thermometer and corresponding numbers (degrees) with hot or cold.
  - Associate the temperature with experiences. *(hot day – swimming)*

TIME

❑ **Learn the concept of time.**

- Identify an event as before or after another.
- Identify an event as longer or shorter than another.
- Name days in a week, months of the year, numbers in a month.
- Read and use a calendar to solve problems.

❑ **Read a clock.** *(Teach after children can identify numerals 1 – 12.)*

- Tell time to the hour. *(Kindergarten)*
- Tell time to the half hour. *(Grade 1)*
- Tell time to the quarter hour. *(Grade 2)*
- Tell time through 5 minute intervals. *(Grade 2)*
- Relate time on a clock to an event.

GEOMETRY AND SPATIAL SENSE

Use concrete objects before pictures.

❑ **Learn concepts.**

- Identify shapes.
- Compare shapes as same or different.
- Identify solids.
- Identify shapes as congruent or not.
- Match congruent figures.
- Identify symmetry in a figure.

❑ **Identify:**

- Shapes: circle, square, triangle, rectangle.
- Solids: ball *(sphere)*, box *(cube)*, can *(cylinder)*, cone, pyramid.
- Associate a drawing with the actual object.
- Identify sides and corners of a figure.
- Identify inside (interior), outside (exterior) of figure. *(Grade 1)*

❑ **Make or draw shapes.**

- Draw shapes: circle, square, triangle, rectangle.
- Make solids using patterns (fold paper). *(Grade 1)*
- Make congruent figures on a geoboard. *(Grade 1)*

FRACTIONS

❑ **Understand fractions as a whole and equal parts of a whole for a region (area) and a group (set).**

❑ **Identify parts of a group (set).**

- Identify parts of a group as halves.
- Identify parts of a group as thirds, fourths. *(Grade 1)*
- Divide a group of objects *(a set)* into halves, thirds, fourths. *(Grade 1)*

❑ **Identify parts of a whole.**

- Identify parts of a whole: halves *(K)*, thirds, fourths. *(Grade 1)*
- Find equal parts of a whole. *(Grade 2)*

TEACHING K – 2 OBJECTIVES

TOPIC: **DEVELOP PROBLEM SOLVING SKILLS**

K-2 OBJECTIVES: Locate objects according to position and direction in space.

Locate objects according to position and direction in two dimensions.

A student must be able to form a mental picture of a problem. Experience ensures understanding of basic vocabulary.

up	down	near	far	before	after	behind
over	under	inside	outside	highest	lowest	next to
above	below	between	in front of	in the middle	right	left

Use the child's own body as the point of reference. *"Put the block under your foot."* Later, use the terms in reference to objects: *"Put the block under the box."* Once that is understood work in two dimensions. Remember that top and bottom and up and down are very different on paper and the child may become confused. When teaching right and left, tie a ribbon to the child's right arm and leg during activities.

Practice

Position and directions in space:

1. Throw balls up (catch) and/or into a large container (clothes basket).

2. Play relay games. *(Give oral directions. E.g., "Line up in front of [or behind] ___.")*

3. Play Simon Says. *(Give directions. E.g., "Hold up your right foot," or "Bend down low.")*

4. Play Follow the Leader. *(Give oral directions.)*

5. Move to music: march *(call out, "right-left-right-left")*, do the Hokey Pokey *(in/out)*, call out action *("swing arms up/down, slap your right knee")*.

6. Give directions for body movement. *(E.g., "Sit on the chair near the door.")*

7. Give directions using objects. *(E.g., "Place the block inside the box.")*

8. Provide an obstacle course, call out directions: go under the table and over the chair.

Position and direction in two dimensions.

1. Use cutouts and a flannel board. Have the student place objects according to the teacher's directions. *(E.g., "Put the dog next to the barn.")*

2. Arrange pictures according to the concept being practiced. Group everything found up in the sky *(e.g., bird, kite, balloon, jet).* Group everything found down or below *(e.g., fish, submarine, diver, coral).*

3. Use pegboards: mark the beginning and end of a row with a peg, then have the child fill in the missing pegs from left to right or top to bottom.

4. Have the child draw according to instructions: Combine practice of shapes when the child is ready. *(E.g., "Draw an X in the middle of the paper. Draw a circle above the X.")*

5. Follow directions on simple maps (north/up, south/down, east/right, west/left).

6. Combine practice with same and different or color and size concepts.
   (E.g., "Color the duck next to the pond yellow. Color the sun above the pond orange.")

K-2 OBJECTIVE: **Make comparisons.**

same	different	longer	longest	heavier	lighter
smaller	smallest	larger	largest	holds more	holds less
shorter	shortest	taller	tallest	more in a group	less in a group

Young children enjoy comparing themselves to others. *"Who is taller?" "Who has the largest hand?"* Use these words in a variety of situations, not just during math class. This vocabulary can be taught while meeting objectives in counting, measuring, time, geometry, and collecting and recording information. *(Refer to these topics for more activity ideas.)*

Practice

1. Put items in a bag and have the child find the one described by touch alone.
   (Vocabulary. E.g., biggest, longest, the one with flat sides, etc.)

2. Which group (set) has more? *(Counting)*

3. Compare shapes. (Use attribute blocks, models.) *(Geometry)*
   How are they the same?
   How are they different?
   Are any sides longer than other sides?

4. Guess and check. *(That is, estimate and measure.)*
   Which is heavier?   (Check with a balance scale.)
   Who is taller?   (Check by placing objects or students next to each other.)
   Which holds more?   (K: use objects to fill the container and check by counting.)

Refer to suggested activities listed in other topics for more ideas.

Compare and/or Order

These are terms used in teaching number concepts. At every level, students are asked to compare two numbers or two sets (groups of objects). At first they use the vocabulary: more than, less than, and the same. Then they use the mathematical terms "greater than" (>), "less than" (<), and "equal to" (=) and their symbols.

Order refers to the arrangement of sets of objects or numbers from least to greatest.

K-2 OBJECTIVE: **Classify and sort according to sameness of kind, color, size, and shape.**

Classification is simply grouping objects that have some property in common. Students should decide whether or not an object belongs to a group—does it have the same property as all the other members of the group? They should also have opportunities to look at a group of objects and figure out why they are put together as a set. These skills are basic to mathematical reasoning. At this level most math activities involve the properties of color, size, and shape, and reinforce objectives in measurement. Kind refers to such labels as all animals, all fruits, or all children. Many of these activities are part of language arts materials.

Before classifying, it is necessary that children recognize color, size, and shape.

⇛ Use concrete examples before using pictures of familiar objects.

⇛ Begin with two objects different in color, shape, or size, then go on to three or more.

⇛ Introduce more than one difference gradually. Eventually, objects can be different in every way but one. For instance, begin with two objects that are the same color, same texture, similar in size, but a different shape.

Recognizing colors

Introduce one color at a time, beginning with the primary colors (red, yellow, blue), followed by secondary colors (green, orange, purple), then black, brown, white, and pink.

Use activities 1 - 4 below with the color, then introduce another color. The first color does not need to be mastered before moving on, just be sure to provide continued review.

1. Match the color of objects or pictures to a color card or place items on a piece of colored construction paper *(same/different)*.

2. Sort items *(blocks, beads, pegs)* on the basis of color. Since this can be done by matching, it is not necessary for the child to be able to identify the color at first.

3. Collect items on the basis of color. First concrete items, later pictures. He could cut out pictures in a magazine if you wanted to combine practice with cutting.

4. Ask the child to find or name items associated with a color *(yellow- sun)*.

5. Play games using color. (E.g., *Color Bingo, Candyland, Color Concentration*.)

6. Relate color to number recognition with color (or paint)-by-number pictures.

At first the child indicates that he is aware of colors that are alike or different, and of items he associates with a color. However, eventually he must be able to name that color consistently.

Recognizing size

1. Teach size as relative.
   Let the child compare an object to himself (*"bigger than me"*) or to another object.
   Use an item once considered "big" as the small item in another comparison.

2. Gradually introduce middle size.

3. Have children arrange objects from smallest to largest. (2 objects, then 3, then more.)

4. Reinforce geometry by using shapes for activities.

5. Reinforce measurement by comparing sizes of things to be used in measurement activities.

6. Reinforce understanding with manipulatives *(e.g., stacking rings, nesting boxes)*.

7. Read and act out stories using size. (E.g., *Three Billy Goats Gruff; Goldilocks and the Three Bears.)*

Recognizing shapes
circle, square, triangle, rectangle

The ability to differentiate shapes is necessary to recognizing letters of the alphabet and is, therefore, often a part of Reading Readiness programs. There is no one correct time to name a shape. If using a discovery approach, you may want the children to carry out activities 1 and 2 below before telling the names. However, the children may already know the names from listening to older brothers and sisters. It is only important that they eventually recognize shapes.

1. Children first learn to see the whole shape. Have children sort shapes into piles of "shapes that are the same." Use two to four different shapes, but with examples of each that are identical.

2. Next children begin to analyze the properties of a shape so that they can recognize a shape even though it may be a different size or in a different position. Let them analyze by sorting objects as belonging, or not belonging, to the pile of a particular shape. During this analysis they should turn the shape various directions so that they begin to recognize that the properties are independent of position. Give them objects that vary at least in size.

3. Have the children find examples of shapes within their environment and, later, in pictures.

   circles   full moon, clock face, CD, bottle top, drawings: a ball, the sun

   rectangles   table top, switch plate, place mat, picture of football field, book

4. Once solid pictures are recognized, introduce outlines of shapes. When outlines are recognized the child can reproduce them on a geoboard. Eventually they should be able to draw the basic shapes.

Classify and sort using sets

The term *set* is used to refer to a specific group of things and is a part of the math vocabulary children must learn. The student looks at an object (or picture or idea) and decides whether or not it belongs to that set. Those things that belong are called *members* of the set. When two sets are combined it is referred to as the *union* of two sets. If a group of some items in a set make up another set as well, they are referred to as a *subset*. These concepts can be practiced in logic books. At this age, the focus remains on the development of comprehension of the idea of a set and the classification process of deciding what belongs and what does not.

Example Sort by shape

Set 1:   red and blue circles *(members of set one)*   Set 2:   yellow triangles *(members)*
Subset: red circles Subset: blue circles

Union of set 1 and 2 (making one new set):   red circles, blue circles, yellow triangles.

Practice

Attribute blocks and activity books reinforce the concepts of set, comparing and classifying, as well as providing experience with the properties of shapes. Attributes are characteristics: color, size, shape, weight, position, use, texture, taste, smell, number of sides, and so on. *(Attribute blocks are available for purchase. See "Supplies," page 13.)*

1. Let children choose the property to use in sorting. Have them tell you their rule (the attribute). *(E.g., "They are all red." "These are heavy, these are light.")*

2. Give the students a small set of items and ask what properties they have in common. If necessary ask leading questions: *"Are they all the same size?" "The same color?" "The same shape?"* They may have several properties in common.

3. Set out four to six objects or pictures. Have the student find the one that does not belong.

4. Name objects, or show pictures, and ask why they belong together. *(E.g., a bird, kite, and jet can all be found in the sky. A knife, fork, and spoon are all used for eating.)*

5. Use the comparison vocabulary as the basis for sorting objects or pictures into one of two groups. *(E.g., things that are heavy and things that are light.)*

6. Sort with more than one attribute *(and)*. *(E.g., blocks that are red and square.)*

7. Sort based on a choice *(or)*. *(E.g., blocks that are red or square.)*

K-2 OBJECTIVE: **Identify and use patterns.**

Visual and/or number patterns are used to make predictions and to classify information.

1. Place 3 to 6 objects or pictures in a sequence (a row) and have the child decide what comes next. Color and shape are frequently used as the pattern to be discovered.

    Offer a choice of three or four objects or pictures to place next. (One correct choice.) Progress toward completing the pattern without limited choices.
    Example: blue bead, red bead, blue bead, *what's next?*

2. Allow children to make up their own patterns, letting someone else complete them. Have the creator identify the property used.

3. Relate patterns to other topics.

   Measurement   heavy, light, light, heavy, heavy, light
   long, long, short, long, long

   Geometry   circle, square, circle, square

   Size   small, bigger, biggest, small, bigger, biggest

4. Have children choose and follow a pattern in art activities.
   - Christmas paper chain for the tree.
   - String beads for a necklace or bracelet.

5. Provide practice with pattern designs (not sequences). This helps develop a sense of parts to whole (*fractions*). Parquetry blocks are a popular manipulative for this activity. *(These are available for purchase. Refer to "Supplies," page 13.)*

6. Provide guided practice looking for patterns with numbers. This will become the primary use of patterns later and is used to discover generalizations or rules. *(E.g., the counting concept on page 44.)* Problems can reinforce various areas of math. The following example reinforces time (learning the days of the week) and the use of charts.

   Problem   Bryan collects baseball cards. On Monday he bought 2 cards. On Tuesday he bought 4 cards. On Wednesday he bought 6 cards. If he continues buying in this pattern, how many cards will he have on Friday?

Provide a chart to help the child find the solution.

Monday	Tuesday	Wednesday	Thursday	Friday	Total
2	4	6			

Filling in the pattern, he writes 8 under Thursday and 10 under Friday. He then adds all the numbers to find the total *(30)*.

Use this model and insert various patterns. Reinforce calendar concepts by using months as well as days.

K-2 OBJECTIVE: Make and check an estimate.

This technique is a basic part of mathematics and should be practiced within every topic. It is used to help develop a sense of quantity (number sense) and spatial awareness, as well as to determine the reasonableness of an answer. As adults, we probably use this skill even more often than we carry out actual calculations.

Estimate does not mean *wild* guesses. Rather, children, by experience, become aware of an acceptable range of answers. Guessing (estimating) the answer that turns out to be the exact answer is no better than guessing (estimating) within the range agreed upon as acceptable.

Deciding on an acceptable range depends on what is being estimated. When buying groceries we might round each item to the nearest fifty cents, or dollar, to have a general sense of the total bill before check out. If we have fifty dollars to spend, the acceptable range would be below fifty, say 46 to 50 dollars. In making our estimate it would be worthless to round our items to the nearest ten dollars. If we are looking at houses to buy, we may mentally note which furniture would fit into a room. Will the living room be large enough for the sectional sofa? Here our mental range would be within one or two feet. When seeking employment a quick mental estimate of our monthly bills within a range of 100 to 200 dollars would be helpful when being told the salary. That is, will the pay be sufficient?

Children need experiences to build skill in making estimates. They need to guess, then check and discuss what would be an acceptable guess. Then they must have follow up experiences that provide practice for what they have just learned. How many beans in the jar? How many blocks in the can? How many books on the shelf? How many feet long is the rope? How many feet long is the room?

Once they learn basic operations (addition, subtraction, multiplication, division), they should also learn specific estimation strategies that will help them decide if an answer is reasonable. It is this skill that will allow them to use a calculator and feel confident that an answer is accurate.

ESTIMATION STRATEGIES TAUGHT AT THE PRIMARY LEVEL

Use of a reference

If a student is asked to guess the number of beans in a jar, he may be given a full cup labeled 100 beans. He mentally imagines how many cupfuls that it would take to fill the jar. Six cupfuls would give him an answer of 600. The labeled cup is the reference.

Chunking

The student puts together several units to make one "chunk" and uses that to help get a total. This is used in measuring. To figure out how many boxes would cover the floor, a row would be set against one side. That number of boxes (say 7) would be a "chunk" and the student would now mentally estimate how many chunks would fill the space. (Perhaps 6 more rows.) And then recall that each of those 7 rows has 7 boxes. He would guess 49 boxes would cover the floor, and then use boxes to check.

Front-end estimation

In adding large numbers, the student looks at the largest place value, adds, then estimates the amount left and adds that to the first number. 392 + 221 would be mentally added as *"300 plus 200 is 500 and 92 plus 21 is just over 100, so the answer is about 600."*

K-2 OBJECTIVE: **Solve one-step word problems requiring a choice between addition and subtraction.**

At this level, children should be given simple problems in which they are to either add or subtract to find the answer. Young students may need to use manipulatives to act out the problem. As a student is able, teach him to write a number sentence and then solve it.

Include unnecessary information (in this case, the color of the balloons) and vary the phrasing of the final question. If all problems end with "altogether" or "in all" for addition, or "how many are left?" for subtraction, students may decide on a shortcut that will lead to errors later. Instead of carefully thinking through the problem, they look for those key words and automatically add.

Point out the action. Jim <u>gave</u> Bob balloons. That means Bob has <u>more</u> than he had before, so he must add. John borrows (takes) two books, so fewer remain on the shelf, and he must subtract.

> Bob had 4 blue balloons. Jim gave him 2 yellow balloons. How many balloons did Bob have then?   Write: 4 + 2 =   Add to find the sum.

> There are five books about seahorses in the library. If John borrows two for his report, how many will remain on the shelves?   Write: 5 - 2 =   Subtract to find the difference.

 TEACH STUDENTS HOW TO APPROACH A PROBLEM.
Direct their thinking as follows:

1. Tell me the problem in your own words.
2. What do you need to find out?
3. Do you have all the information you need?
4. Is there any information that you don't need?
5. Should you plan to add or subtract? What tells you that you should add? subtract?
6. Draw a picture or use manipulatives to show what you need to do.
Once the student solves the problem:
7. Have you checked your arithmetic? (Counted twice, for instance.)
8. Does your answer make sense? (Is it reasonable?)

Do all or any portion of this procedure until the student is able to reason on his own.

K-2 OBJECTIVE: Collect, record, and interpret information.

Provide opportunities for students to work in a group to collect and record data. This gives them hands-on experience with graphs, charts, and tables. There are suggestions throughout this guide to combine these experiences with learning in other areas. At this level, children work in a group. The teacher tells them which information is to be collected, labels the chart to help them remember what they are looking for, and asks questions directing an analysis of the information and leading to conclusions.

Collect   What information is to be collected?

Record   How should it be displayed so that someone looking at it will understand?

Analyze   Are there any patterns?
Were the results expected or a surprise?
Can you make a prediction?
Can you make a generalization?

Practice

1. **Take a survey.**

   Children can participate in choosing the information to be collected. What would they like to know? They ask each person in the class, or in whatever group is being surveyed. For example, are there more students with blue eyes or brown eyes?

   Tally results.

   Place pictures (or numbers) across the top of the chart to represent the choices (or words they can read) and draw tally marks (single strokes) in the appropriate column as students offer information. Add the tallies in each column, writing the total (the results) at the bottom of the column.

blue eyes	brown eyes
‖‖‖ ‖‖	‖‖‖‖ ‖‖‖‖
7	‖ 11

   Analyze results.

   What are the results? *"Are there more students with blue eyes or brown?"*
   Is that what you thought?
   Based on the results, if a new classmate was to arrive, would he be more likely to have ____ (brown eyes or blue). *(Probability)*

---

2. **Collect, record, and interpret information in a science experiment.**

Refer to page 85 for examples using a pictograph and a bar graph.

K-2 OBJECTIVE: **Make up (create) problems when given information.**

Use real-life situations more than workbook problems with young children. They are learning to recognize and identify a problem which can then be solved.

Practice

1. At snack time, give a group of 5 children 10 crackers and ask them to make up a problem for that situation. *"There are 5 of us and we each want the same amount of crackers."* Then they think of ways to solve that problem: handing each person one cracker until they run out of crackers; figuring out the problem mentally or with a pencil and paper, and so on.

2. Give information and ask for a problem: *"We have two nickels and five dimes. The notebook costs 89 cents."* Given that information the student makes up a problem: *"Do we have enough money to buy the notebook?"*

K-2 OBJECTIVE: **Use a calculator.**

1. When the focus is on reasoning have students look for patterns or verify a generalization by trying to find out if it appears to "always work."

2. When the student needs to focus on learning the procedure for solving a problem.

3. When checking work.

K-2 OBJECTIVE: **Use a computer.**

Use software programs to give the children opportunities for problem solving and practice with math concepts already introduced.

TOPIC: # PROBABILITY AND STATISTICS

Probability

This is simply finding out how likely it is for an event to occur and is expressed as a number over a total (written in fraction form). Something likely to occur 6 out of 20 times would be written $\frac{6}{20}$. Because children enjoy making and testing predictions, this is a popular topic.

Statistics

At this level, collecting, recording and interpreting information is considered preparation for later development with statistics. Children should have experiences with bar graphs, pictographs, and calendars. Incorporate these activities into various topics.

K-2 Objective: **Explore chance.**

K-2 Objective: **Construct a chart or graph.**

K-2 Objective: **Collect and interpret information.**

Refer to *Teaching 3-4: Collect, Record, and Analyze Data,* (see sample graphs page 85).

Practice

1. Use a spinner on a circle divided into 2 or 3 equal colored sections. Predict a color, spin, record the color pointed to by the spinner.

2. Use coins. Predict heads or tails, toss, and record results. (This activity may be included during the study of money, page 60.)

3. Use number cubes. Predict a number, toss the cube, and then record the results. *(Reading numbers.)*

Making the Chart

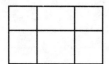

Help the children make a chart to record results. The column heading should be a picture (color and shape on the spinner, play money coin, numeral) and the students should place a tally mark in the appropriate column after each spin or toss.

Recording Results

4	6	5
IIII	IIIIII	IIIII
$\frac{4}{10}$	$\frac{6}{10}$	$\frac{5}{10}$

After a number of tallies, the students should count the tally marks and write (or have the teacher write) the total within each column. Under that number would be the total number of tosses. Draw a fraction line between the two numbers.

If the coin was flipped 10 times and there are four tally marks in the heads column, the result would be written $\frac{4}{10}$. Out of ten tosses, four were heads.

Reviewing Results

1. When you (spin, flip, toss) are you more likely to get (name choices)?

2. If you (spin, flip, toss) (#) times, how many (reds, heads, fives) do you think you might get? (If they had 10 tosses, ask *"If you did it 20 times? 30 times?"* to help look for patterns to use in making predictions.)

3. Find out if you are right. *(Let students experiment to find out if this prediction is true.)*

K-1 TOPIC:	**UNDERSTANDING NUMBERS 0 - 20**

K-1 OBJECTIVE:	**Recognize, name, write, compare, and order numbers 0 - 20.**

Background   Experience comparing, ordering, and classifying objects.

Materials   A variety of objects for counting
Number cards: 0 - 20   Print one number on each card.
Symbol cards: +, −, = , <. >   Print one symbol on each card.

Use a few numbers for all of the activities before moving on to larger numbers. 1 - 4 to count, compare, order, match, and identify the next number. Then 0, 5 - 8; review 0 - 8, teach 9 - 12, review 1 - 12, then 13 - 20.

Counting   Gradually count up to 30 objects: to five, then to ten, and so on.

1. Use a variety of objects so that a number is not associated with a specific item.

2. Have the child touch and separate the item as he says the number.
   (Moving the counter to a separate part of the table prevents confusion.)

3. Rearrange objects and have them counted a second time: a row to a pile or a rearranged row.

Understanding Quantity

1. Children must recognize that position does not affect quantity. Check by having two equal rows of 4 items. Use the same type of counter in each row. Place the rows one above the other but spread out the objects in the top row. Ask which row has more. If the child equates more space with greater quantity, carry out more activities until he understands correctly.

2. Give students directions involving quantities. *"Put two cups on the table." "Give me five sheets of paper."* This brings math into the real world and prevents children from identifying an object as "one" or "two" rather than recognizing quantity.

3. Help children discover the **counting concept**: *each number is one more than the previous number.* (Some may have already discovered it on their own.)

Put number cards 1 - 12 in a row and the corresponding number of objects in a column under each card for numbers 1 – 4 (or glue pictures to a chart.) Make sure the 1st, 2nd, 3rd, etc., object in each column lines up horizontally with its neighbor so that it is easily observed that each column has one more than the previous column.

1	2	3	4	5	6	7	8	9	10	11	12

Direct students' thinking:

1. How many more are in the 2 column than the 1 column?
2. How many more under 3 than 2?
3. So, how many more do you think 5 will have than 4?
4. Let's see. (Put five in a column and check.)
5. What about 6? How many more will it have than 5?
6. What happens when we count?

Students make a generalization: We add one to count to the next number.

Compare and Order Sets and Numbers

1. Compare two sets (groups). Use objects before pictures.

   Children should guess which pile (set) of objects has more? fewer? This gives practice in estimating and helps develop an understanding of quantity.

   Checking the guess

   Have children check their guess by matching one item from each set physically, moving them together as a pair. If using pictures, draw a line connecting one from each group. This is called **one-to-one correspondence.** *The set with more will have objects left unmatched.*

   OR

   Have children check by counting objects in a group, and then, remembering quantity, tell which has more (or less). *"This has 5, this has 3 and 3 is less than 5."* If they give a wrong answer, have them check their guess by using one-to-one correspondence.

2. Compare two numbers.

Give students two numbers. The students should make a set of objects, or draw a picture illustrating each number, and then compare sets by matching or counting.

OR

Given two numbers, tell from memory which is greater. Which is less than the other?

Eventually use the terms greater than >, less than <, and equal to = and their symbols. It may help to equate < and > with a mouth open to gobble the bigger number: 3 > 2; 2 < 3.

3. Order sets of objects from least to greatest. Place left to right. Use 3 to 5 sets.

4. Order numbers.

Arrange from 3 to 5 numbers in order from least to greatest, left to right. This may first be done by matching each number to a group of objects and then arranging the groups. Then, match each number to an illustration (or draw on the number card) and arrange. Eventually, the students should be able to arrange the number cards without any manipulatives. They should have a mental image of the quantity.

Match the numeral to its set.
Match objects in a group (set) to a choice of 2 or 3 number cards.

If this proves difficult, draw objects on the back of the number cards (4 circles on the 4 card) so they can check the guess. They can match their counters to each picture. If necessary, use large number cards so that they can physically place each counter on top of a picture to check their work.

Teach the **concept of zero** <u>after</u> they have associated quantities and symbols with a few numbers (1-4, perhaps). Zero is introduced as *none* or *not any*. It is most easily understood in contrast to quantities already learned. *"I have 2 pennies in this hand. I don't have any pennies in this hand."*

1. Give the student a group of objects. *"How many (blocks) do you have?"* *"Point to the numeral that shows how many you have."*

2. Give students directions but hold up a number card instead of saying the number.

3. Work toward writing a numeral to show how many are in a set. They will need practice tracing a numeral with their finger, then with a pencil, before writing it from memory. Eventually students should be able to write a number on command without looking at a picture. *"Write the numeral five on the paper."*

4. Relate numbers to time: trace numerals on a calendar.

5. Read number words *(grade one)*—match numeral to word card.

Identify the next number forward, backward, between.

1. First, help children identify the next number forward *without* counting from one. Put number cards down in order, but number side down. Turn over a card. *"What is this number?"* (3) *"What number is next?"* (4) *"Turn over the card to the right of the 3 to check."*

2. Give the student 2 sequential number cards. Offer two or three other number cards from which he is to choose the next number back or forward.

   ? 2 3   Fill in 1   2, 3 ?   Fill in 4

3. Identify the number in between 2 numbers.

   4 ? 6   Fill in 5

   Eventually the student should be able to tell you the number before or after any card you hold up without choices or clues.

Practice

1. Connect the dot pictures reinforce number sequence.

2. Relate to the use of a calendar by providing some of the numbers, but leaving squares blank for the student to fill in the correct numeral.

3. Relate to telling time: show a clock face with a few missing numerals to be filled in.

4. Reinforce number sense by giving the child clues to figure out the "mystery" number. Use pictures or manipulatives with young children.

   "The number is more than the triangles in this set (3 triangles) and less than the circles in this set (5 circles). What is the number?"

K-2 OBJECTIVE: **Understand the concepts of *adding to* and *taking away from*.**

K-2 OBJECTIVE: **Associate the symbol + with *adding to*.**
Associate the symbol - with *taking away from*.

Add and Subtract (Take Away) 0 - 6

Use objects, pictures, and, eventually, numbers only. Limit the sets to 6 or less so that the focus remains on understanding what adding and subtracting mean.

ADDITION *Sums through 6. Add only 1 or 2 more at the kindergarten level.*

The student may need to count all the objects at first. Have him work toward *counting on** to get to the answer. Touching the objects as he counts is generally helpful. (*Start with the first number, not one, and count forward. 6 + 3 would be counted "6, 7, 8, 9")

1. Begin with 2 sets of objects. Join the sets using the words "add to" and "how many in all?" or "all together?"

2. Use symbols for plus (+) and equal (= or a bar sign) and have the student choose the number card for the sum after counting. Set up both horizontal and vertical equations.

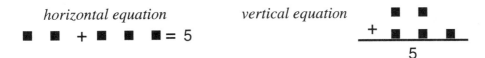

3. Use number cards and symbols. Have them fill in the sum with a number card. To solve the problem, they may put out objects to illustrate the number cards and then count objects.

4. Begin using the terms *plus* and *equal to* along with *and*, and *all together* or *in all* so that students recognize that they mean the same thing. Then use the term sum (in all). Your question can be either *"How many in all?"* or *"What is the sum?"* Use both.

5. Use the same 2 sets but in reverse order to help students discover that the order does not change the sum.

6. Have children practice with all combinations of adding two numbers with sums up to 12. *They should eventually memorize these as addition facts.*

7. Missing addends: provide the answer (sum) but not one of the other numbers (addends). Do this with both word problems and equations using the number cards.

8. Give the student word problems. Have him use manipulatives to find the answer.

9. Give the student word problems and have him use the number cards to illustrate the problem with a number sentence and then find the solution.

10. Provide real life situations to reinforce concepts.

Add by counting on.   Use objects or a number line.

Example: Add 6 + 3

Using objects   Make a set of six and a set of three. Instead of pushing them together and counting each object, point to the set of six and say "six," then touch each object in the set of three while counting forward: "7, 8, 9."

Using a number line Point to the six, then touch each number to the right, saying, "one, two, three." Then note that you are pointing to the number nine.

SUBTRACTION *(take away)   Numerals 0 – 6.*
Take away only 1 or 2 at the kindergarten level

1. Here the student begins with the whole. Have him count the objects in the set. *"Now take (1 or 2) away."* He separates the (1 or 2) objects. *"How many are left?"*

2. Use the number cards and minus symbol with objects, having the student illustrate the problem with manipulatives and either telling the answer, or finding the number card and putting it in the proper place. Set out cards for both vertical and horizontal problems.

3. Give the student word problems to solve using manipulatives.

4. Give the student word problems. Have him find the solution to each by first making a number sentence to illustrate the problem.

5. Help students discover the relationship between addition and subtraction.

    "Put 10 buttons (any small objects) under one hand. Don't look. Now move 4 out onto the table where we can see them. Don't look under your hand. How many buttons are still under your hand? (or, how many buttons do you have left?)" He sees 4, 6 more make 10, so 6 are under his hand. He then checks. *"Yes, 10 take away 4 is 6."*

    "I have some marbles in this can. I'm putting in 7 more. Now I have 10. How many marbles were in the can to start with?" Use whatever numbers the students have learned.

6. Continue with the above understanding using both word problems and number equations with a number other than the answer (difference) missing. **5 - ☐ = 3**

7. Have students write out number equations when they are able rather than using number cards.

8. Provide real life situations to reinforce concepts.

"Here are 2 cookies for you and 3 for me. Who has more? How many do we have all together? How many more do I have?"

Subtract by counting back. Use objects or a number line.

Begin with the first number and count back the quantity represented by the second number.

Example: Subtract 6 - 3.

Using objects   Solve 6 - 3. Make a set of six. Touching each of the three to be removed, say "5, 4, 3."

Using a number line   Touch the six, point to the left "1,2,3," and note you are at the 3.

TOPIC: # UNDERSTANDING NUMBERS 20 - 999

Develop an understanding of quantity through 1,000.

Give children practice estimating (guessing) and checking a variety of quantities using a variety of items.

paper clips in a box	balls in a basket	cups on a table
cubes in a box	cans in a cupboard	keys on a ring
dried beans in a bag	slices of bread in a loaf	pages in a book

Discuss a reasonable range of estimates so that they do not become disappointed at not guessing the exact number. That's not the purpose of estimating. When checking large quantities, have them count 10 items and set the pile aside, later counting by tens to get the total.

Occasionally use a reference to help them guess. Cubes in a box. First make a layer of cubes in the bottom of the box to be counted. Then ask how many it would take to fill the box.

K-2 OBJECTIVE: **Recognize, name, and write numbers 20 - 999.**

Our number system gives each **place** a **value**, making the placement of a digit important. Numbers are *read, written, compared, ordered and rounded* based on **place value**. If a student has difficulty with computation, check for understanding of place value, it's often the source.

- Use manipulatives to develop an understanding of place value.

- Provide a chart labeling any places being taught during practice reading and writing numbers.

hundreds	tens	ones

- Have students memorize the name of each place from right to left (for whole numbers).

Manipulatives   Connecting cubes (cubes which fit together)
Straws or sticks to bundle
Place value blocks (cubes, rods of ten connected cubes, squares of 100 connected cubes)

Practice

Activities to recognize, name, and write numbers using place value.

Begin with numbers from 20 to 99. The teens are more difficult because of their names. Four tens and three ones sounds similar to forty-three; five tens and two ones sounds close to fifty-two. Teach the teens after the students are familiar with a variety of other two-digit numbers and can count by tens.

1. Students group a pile of more than ten objects into piles of ten, then count by tens to find the total of tens and the number left over. *3 tens and 4 left over.*
    Provide plenty of practice counting by tens to ninety.

2. Tell students to *"Show me ___ tens"* and have them illustrate with manipulatives. *Show me 4 tens.*

3. Tell students to *"Show me ___ tens and ___ left over."* Have students illustrate your instructions with manipulatives.

4. Have the student **estimate** the number in a pile and check by separating objects into piles of ten and counting by tens to check his guess. This helps develop a sense of quantity. He can record his check and practice writing numbers. Provide a chart with two columns. One heading is tens, the other ones. <u>He writes the number of tens he counts, then the number of ones</u>.

 If writing is difficult, let him choose a number card and make pockets on the chart.

tens	ones
3	4
2	6

5. Give the students practice finding or writing numbers for sets and making sets for written numbers. At first the written numbers may read "__ tens and __ones" but at some point progress to illustrations of two-digit numbers.

Continue with activities until the student is able to:

- Look at a model representing a 2-digit number. Say the number and write it.

- Look at a written 2-digit number. Read it out loud, and illustrate it with a model.

- Write a spoken number without using a model. *"Write 64 in the box."*

Continue with these activities to teach hundreds. For example, dictate numbers or have students look at a model and record the number on a chart naming places through the hundreds *(page 50).*

 Let children look for patterns and discover how to write numbers using the following method:

Give the child several sets of tens and ones (from 10 - 40) with the appropriate number card placed next to the set. Have the child count the objects if he doesn't yet know how to read the number. Give him a set without a number card and have him write it by finding the pattern, or choose the correct number card from among several choices. *"Well, the 11 had 1 ten bar and a cube, the 16 had 1 ten bar and 6 cubes, the 23 had 2 ten bars and 3 cubes and the 27 had 2 ten bars and 7 cubes. Since this has 3 ten bars and 5 cubes, I think it would be written 35."* He does not have to be able to read the number to reason through and write or choose the correct answer.

K-2 OBJECTIVE: **Order three and four numbers.**

Use the numbers being taught with place value. Have students arrange 2, 3, then 4 numbers from least to greatest. This requires students to compare two numbers at a time to determine which is more. It also provides practice with the next number forward, backward and in between.

K-2 Objective: **Compare two numbers using place value.**

Once students have practice making sets with tens and ones, they can compare two sets without having to count single objects. Occasionally vary objects used so that children don't associate quantity with any particular object. Check their understanding of quantity by varying the sizes of objects in the two groups being compared.

1. Have students line up two sets, one under the other, so they can quickly see which has more piles of ten. When the tens are the same, have them decide visually which has more ones. They can check by pairing (one-to-one correspondence) items in each set and discovering which set has something left over and, therefore, has more.

2. Introduce numbers and symbols as illustrations for the manipulatives used above. Now each set should start with both a number card and manipulatives. The student will choose from the symbol cards and place it between the number cards (> greater than, < less than). It may help to tell children that the small point is next to the small number or that the big opening is next to the big number.

3. Eventually give students two number cards and the symbol cards. They choose the symbol card and place it between the two numbers. Sets can be made either to solve the problem, or to check their work.

4. Progress to looking at the numbers without using manipulatives. Help the students discover that with two-digit numbers, the larger number in the tens place means that it is the greater number. If those numbers are the same, the larger number in the ones place determines the greater number.

Follow the same procedure for comparing greater numbers.

Topic: # COMPUTATION WITH WHOLE NUMBERS

Teaching Tips:

1. Introduce the concept with manipulatives and/or illustrations.

2. Let the students figure things out. Ask leading questions as often as possible.

3. Provide practice with manipulatives and/or illustrations using a few simple numbers before moving on to larger numbers and/or a wider range of numbers.

4. Encourage eventual memorization of concepts, facts, formulas and procedures after they have been understood (after a great deal of practice and as students are able).

5. Provide practice without manipulatives or illustrations as children are able.

6. The process must eventually become automatic, a habit.

7. Provide review of previously learned material. (Retention requires use.)

8. Build speed in computation, maintaining accuracy, after procedures are well understood.

K-2 OBJECTIVE: **Understand and use properties of addition.**

K-2 OBJECTIVE: **Identify different ways to name a number.**

K-2 OBJECTIVE: **Check work by adding in reverse order.**

Direct student thinking during activities to reach the following conclusions:
(They do not need to know the names of properties.)

⇛ **A number plus zero equals that number.** *(zero property of addition)*

⇛ **Two numbers can be added in any order—it does not change the sum.**
(commutative property of addition: $2 + 3 = 3 + 2$*)*

This is especially handy to know when trying to learn addition facts. If you know 6 plus 4 is ten, then you already know 4 plus 6. Until facts are memorized, students can count on to find sums. They should begin with the largest number, no matter what its position, knowing that order is not important. 4 + 6 would be solved by saying "6, 7, 8, 9, 10."

⇛ **Three or more numbers can be added in any order without changing the sum.**
(associative property of addition)

Numbers are added in pairs. A group of 3 numbers may have parentheses around the two that are to be added first: $(5 + 6) + 2 = 5 + (6 + 2)$. At this age, children practice adding three numbers all less than ten, often arranged vertically and without parentheses. They add the first two numbers, then the third, and then check their work by reversing the order. It is in learning to check their work that they might recognize the truth of the associative property.

⇛ **A number plus one is the next counting number.**

⇛ **One sum can be found using different combinations of numbers.**
To maintain the same sum, increase one addend by one and reduce the other by one.

During practice with addition facts they may notice several combinations with the same sum: 1 + 9; 2 + 8; 3 + 7. By arranging practice problems, you can direct their discovery of the pattern mentioned above. (This can be done with a variety of problems, not just addition facts.)

For example: Row 1: 20 + 6   19 + 7   18 + 8
              Row 2: 225 + 54   224 + 55   223 + 56.

K-2 OBJECTIVE: **Add one-, two-, and three-digit numbers with one- and two-digit numbers, renaming ones.**

1. Use the numbers already covered in place value practice (*Understanding Numbers 20 - 999*). Choose a range of numbers for both addition and subtraction before more difficult addition.

2. To develop a firm grasp of the use of symbols:

Have students illustrate a number sentence with manipulatives and then solve it. Use vertical and horizontal problems.

$$\begin{array}{r} 2 \\ + 3 \\ \hline \end{array}$$ ■■
                    + ■■■   1 + 5 =   ■ + ■■■■■ =

Have students look at an illustration, then write and solve an appropriate number sentence.

🔔🔔🔔🔔🔔 + 🔔🔔🔔🔔 = ☐   5 + 4 = ☐

Have students use a number line to find the sum of two numbers.

A number line can provide a visual aid that can sometimes bridge the gap between using actual objects and writing the sum without aids.

0 1 2 3 4 5 6 7 8 9

4 + 2: Start at 4, move forward 2.
The number you land on is the sum.

3. Include problems with a sum and without an addend. 2 + ☐ = 5

4. Include word problems using addition.

Addition Fact Strategies

Students should practice addition facts (digits 0 - 9, sums through 18) until they are memorized. Write practice problems in a group according to a pattern to make memorization easier.

1. **Doubles** (1 + 1, 2 + 2, 3 + 3)

Divide doubles into two groups: sums ten and under and more than ten.

2. Numbers just 1 away from being doubles: $(2 + 3; 6 + 7)$
Children can count on one if they remember the double of the smaller number, or count back one if they remember the sum of the double of the greater number.
2 and 2 is four, 2 plus 3 must be 5.

3. One digit remains the same. $3 + 1, 1 + 3, 3 + 2, 2 + 3, 3 + 3, 3 + 4, 4 + 3$

Addition with a two-digit number

Have the student use the place value manipulatives, putting out ten bars and ones for each addend. **Teach the procedure for addition: add ones, then tens.** Have them count the ones, then place a number card or write the number under the ones column. Next they should count the ten bars, using a number card or writing the number under the tens column. Continue in this manner when teaching addition involving three-digit numbers.

Addition with renaming
Students should use place value manipulatives.

1. The student illustrates each number with appropriate tens and ones.
2. He first adds the ones and renames them by grouping them into tens. The number left over is recorded in the ones column. The ten bars are "carried" over to join the other tens. The total number of ten bars is recorded in the tens column.

After three-digit numbers have been added without renaming, use the above procedure to introduce renaming tens as well as ones.

K-2 OBJECTIVE: ## Subtract 1-, 2-, and 3-digit numbers from a 3-digit number.

Have children try to subtract in a different order to find out if the commutative property applies to subtraction. (Will 6 - 5 have the same answer as 5 - 6? No.)

1. Use numbers in subtraction that have already been used in addition.

2. Have students begin with manipulatives.

Students begin with a set and are told to take away a specified amount, then find out how many are left. Once they understand the concept, proceed to written problems. They may use manipulatives to find the answer, and either write in the number, or select the correct number card and put it in the space provided for the answer (difference).

3. Provide a number line for solving simple problems.

   Number lines provide practice counting back. The student finds the largest number, then counts back the smaller number. The number at his stopping point is the answer *(difference)*.

4. Have students use place value manipulatives once place value has been introduced and larger numbers recognized.

   The student sets out tens and ones (tens on the left) suggested by the first (horizontal) or top (vertical) number of the written problem. He then looks at the second number, which should only be one-digit at first, and takes away that many ones. He then records his answer.

5. Provide practice for the student to write a number sentence for a problem that is illustrated with pictures or objects.

        The student would write 3 - 1 = 2

6. Provide practice solving word problems. Young children may need to act out the problem in order to analyze the action. As they are able, have them write the problem as a number sentence, and then solve it. **5 - 2 = ☐**

7. Introduce subtraction of a two-digit number from a two-digit number after practice that indicates understanding of the above procedures. *(Generally, some time in first grade.)*

Use place value manipulatives so that students can first solve the problem by taking away ones and then tens. As subtraction facts are mastered, the student should be able to write answers simply by subtracting in the ones column, and then the tens column without using objects.

<u>*Until facts are memorized,*</u> encourage students to count up instead of taking away and then counting the remaining objects from one. The student looks at the lesser number, says it, pauses, then counts up using his fingers: 9 – 7 would be "7 to 8 (holds up one finger), 9 (holds up another finger). Now he looks at his two fingers— the answer is two. Be sure that he does not start holding up fingers when he says the first number.

Subtraction Fact Strategies
Help students notice patterns by providing practice with groups that illustrate a pattern.

1. A row where <u>**one**</u> is the number being subtracted. *Pattern* Count back one.

2. A row where **zero** is the number being subtracted. *Pattern* You still have the same amount.

3. A row with the same number subtracted and the top numbers increasing by one.

$$\begin{array}{ccc} 4 & 5 & 6 \\ -\,2 & -\,2 & -\,2 \\ \hline \end{array}$$

Pattern The answers increase by one as the top number increases by one.
Pattern The answers decrease by one as the top number decreases by one.

This pattern is helpful when some facts are memorized and the student is faced with one that he does not remember that is one more or less. For instance, he remembers 12 - 6 but is faced with 11 - 6. Now he just takes one away from his 12 - 6 answer.

4. Relate subtraction facts to addition. *Pattern* The answer (difference) plus the number being subtracted gives you the number with which you started.

If the student can answer 3 + 2 = 5, then he can find the answer to 5 − 2 by asking himself what added to 2 is 5, and remembering 3.

K-2 OBJECTIVE: **Subtract, renaming ones and tens.**

Introduce renaming only after students are comfortable subtracting with two- and three-digit numbers. Use numbers 1 - 9 subtracted from two-digit numbers. Provide place value manipulatives for students to illustrate the 2-digit number. When they see that they can no longer simply take away from each group (ones, tens), ask them what they can do. Direct their thinking to trading a ten bar for ten ones. Now they can take away and count the number left. Those students ready for the next step can be shown how to write this. (Refer to *Teaching Grades 3 – 4,* page 97.)

K-2 OBJECTIVE: **Understand that multiplication is adding like numbers.**
                                  (Repeated addition)

K-2 OBJECTIVE: **Multiplication through 5 times a 1-digit number.**

1. Begin with real life situations and concrete objects (quantities 1 - 5).

    "There are four plates on the table. Each plate has 2 cookies. How many cookies in all?"

    Children can count by twos (four twos or four times two is eight).

    Use the same four plates and change the number of cookies (or whatever you are using). Remember, each plate must have the same number of cookies.

2. Put a full egg carton out. How many rows? (2) How many eggs in each row? (6)
   How many eggs? (6 + 6) or (2 x 6)

3. Have children practice counting by twos, threes, fours and fives to find answers; later, practice counting by sixes through nines. (Count up to twelve times a number.)

4. Use sets of objects and introduce symbols.
   Put out two, three, or four sets of objects. Using number cards, show the student how to make the number sentence with the multiplication symbol, and how to write it as an addition problem. Horizontal equations are usually encountered first. Teach the vertical as well.

   Horizontal   *"There are 3 sets"* (take the 3 card) *"and there are four in each set."* (Take the four card.) *"So we write 3 x 4."* (Place the symbol card between the number cards.) *"That says the same thing as if we added. How would we add these?"* *"Yes, four, plus four, plus four."* (Use number cards and plus signs: 4 + 4 + 4) *"How many fours do we have?"* *"Yes, three."*

   Vertical   3 sets of 4 objects. The number <u>in</u> the set goes on top; the number of sets is next to the multiplication symbol. *"3 times 4 objects"*   4
                                                                                        x 3

5. Provide sets, number cards, and the multiplication symbol card (or they can write the problem if able). Have students solve both vertical and horizontal problems.

   ⇛ Students write (put out the cards) the expressions for given sets.

   ⇛ Students then find "how many in all?" and write the total.

   ⇛ Students make sets for a problem, then solve and record the total.

   2 x 3   **OOO**   **OOO**   2 x 3 = 6

   ⇛ Students make their own sets and equations. (Here they may want to use higher numbers.)

6. Give the students word problems to illustrate: *I have four cups and two ice cubes in each cup* (4 groups, 2 in each group: 4 x 2). If they can't write the expression from the words, have them act it out and then write it.

7. Encourage students to look for patterns.
   Students may need to place objects on a tray and turn the tray to see that the rows and number in each row depend on how you look at them. (It is the *commutative property*

of multiplication: two numbers can be multiplied in any order. For now, they are discovering this generalization, but don't need to remember the name.)

$2 \times 4 = 8$ ΔΔΔΔ
ΔΔΔΔ

$4 \times 2 = 8$ ΔΔ
ΔΔ
ΔΔ
ΔΔ

8. Continue the above activities with numbers through nine. Children age 8 or older should then practice counting by sixes through nines (up to twelve of each).

Grade 2 Objectives

• Match a written multiplication problem to an illustration.

• Match a written multiplication problem to an addition problem.

• Multiply numbers 1 - 9 by 2, 3, 4, and 5.

• Solve word problems using multiplication, writing the appropriate number sentence.

K-2 Objective: **Division as a concept of separation.**

Multiplication combined equal groups. Division separates a set into equal groups (subsets).

Begin with word problems students can discuss and/or use manipulatives to solve.

Sharing   I have 10 pretzels for 2 children. How many pretzels will each child get? The box has 12 markers. There are 3 children. How many markers for each?

Grouping   There are 8 pens. Each student gets two. How many students will get pens?

Students may need to act out each situation, passing out items and then counting the number in each pile. Number and symbol cards may be used as in K-2 activities *(pages 45-48).*

TOPIC:	**MONEY**

K-2 OBJECTIVE: **Identify a coin and its value: penny, nickel, dime, quarter, half-dollar.**

K-2 Objective: **Compare two coins in value.**

K-2 Objective: **Add pennies up to twenty cents.**

K-2 Objective: **Match coins to a price up to thirty cents.**

Materials pennies, nickels, dimes, quarters, half-dollars
number cards 1 - 12 with the cent symbol after the number

Teaching Tip *Coordinate with numbers taught in Understanding Numbers 0 - 20.*

PRACTICE

(Also see page 42, #2.)

Use the following activities with pennies, later add nickels, then dimes. Quarters and dimes are often introduced at ages 6 and 7.

1. Count pennies, up to ten or twelve cents.

2. Compare two sets of pennies: which has more?

3. Match pennies to number cards.
   This is more fun if the cards are set next to objects as if they are the price for sale.
   The child puts the correct number of pennies next to each number card.

4. Add up to ten cents. Children choose two items, place the pennies on each price card, and count to find the total.

5. Have children compare two prices. Which is more? Let them use pennies to decide or to check their work.

When introducing other coins to use in the above activities, match it only to the card with its value (nickel to the 5¢ card, dime to the 10¢) at first. When the children find totals they should begin with only one coin other than pennies and find the total by **counting on**. That is, beginning with the coin of largest value, they say the amount, then touch each penny counting one more. For example, a dime and 4 pennies would be "ten, eleven, twelve, thirteen, fourteen." The nickel and dime are generally introduced within a few days of each other.

Give children various quantities of nickels or dimes to provide practice in counting by fives or tens. If this proves too difficult, let them count by fives or tens with groups of pennies so when confused they can check by touching each penny in a group and counting on. Once they can count by fives, have them count totals made up of nickels and pennies. When they can count by tens, give them dimes and pennies to total.

Once children are familiar with the coins and counting, begin to mix coins for totals. Now a nickel, dime and penny can be counted as 16 cents, not only a dime and six pennies. *Do this before introducing the quarter and half-dollar unless the child is especially able. Quarters and half-dollars are generally used with children at about age seven.*

K-2 OBJECTIVE: **Solve money problems using addition, no renaming.**

K-2 OBJECTIVE: **Solve money problems using subtraction, no renaming.**

K-2 OBJECTIVE: **Make change up to twenty-five cents.**

K-2 OBJECTIVE: **Solve word problems requiring addition or subtraction of money with answers less than ten dollars.**

Meet the above objectives with games and playing store rather than through workbook materials. Keep the lesson time interesting and enjoyable.

PRACTICE

1. Encourage the children to reason. Hide a number of coins in your hand, telling the children how many you have. Tell them the total value of the coins. Let them figure out the possible combinations of coins you might have. *"I have three coins. They total 16 cents. What are they?"*

   If the children have difficulty, show them one coin. If they still can't reason it through, use two coin combinations for a while. If they find three easy, use four coin combinations.

2. To combine money objectives with probability, begin with a number of covered coins, not telling the number of coins, but telling which coins. *"I have pennies, nickels and dimes in this bowl. I'm going to pull out (#) coins. Could I have (amount) in my hand?"*

   Have the children make a chart of possible combinations that could be in your hand or that they could take out of the bowl. Use two, then three coins. Use four when students are able.

TOPIC:	**MEASUREMENT**

K-2 OBJECTIVE: **Understand the concept of measuring.**

K-2 OBJECTIVE: **Understand attributes of temperature, length, capacity, and weight.**

At this age, *emphasis must be on the experiences that build understanding,* not on formal instruments or formulas. Begin with a variety of informal units so that children understand what measuring means before memorizing procedures or formal units. As children practice measuring, help them realize the need for defined units. For example, everyone, including the teacher, could measure the length of the same item with their own hand. Have students look at the variety of responses—asking if everyone got the same results. Have everyone measure the same item again using each person's foot—again having students note the variety of responses. Then give everyone string that has been cut into identical lengths. Ask if they think their results will match—then have them measure and compare results to check their prediction.

Regular practice estimating, then checking, is necessary to develop a sense of a unit. Students should eventually be able to estimate a variety of measures—mentally picturing how many basketballs could fit into a basket, or how many rulers would fit across their bed, for example. When the student checks his guess, show him how to measure accurately *(page 64).*

K-2 OBJECTIVE: **Understand attributes of temperature.**
Recognize temperature as hot or cold.
(hotter, hottest, colder, coldest)

K-2 OBJECTIVE: **Identify the red line on a thermometer and the corresponding number (degrees) with hot or cold.**
Associate temperature with experiences.
(Build a snowman, swim.)

Relate temperature to real life.

1. Associate temperature with the words hot, hotter, hottest, cold, colder, coldest. *This is easily accomplished during other lessons: cooking, science, calendar.*

Is the water hot or cold?	Which cup of water is hotter?
Is it a hot day?	A cold day?

2. Have children read a thermometer to find the temperature outside and inside. Let them check baking temperature on the oven dial, cocoa with a candy thermometer, and so on.

3. First grade workbooks sometimes include pictures of a thermometer with a red line and the temperature marked. Students then choose from two or three pictures of situations, only one of which would be true of that temperature. A thermometer marked 85 degrees may offer a picture of someone swimming and one of a snowman as choices. This can be adapted by giving a student pictures and having him color a red line on a thermometer drawn on a marker board.

K-2 OBJECTIVE: **Understand attributes of length, capacity, and weight.**

      ❏   **Guess and compare to check.**
      ❏   **Measure using informal units.**
      ❏   **Measure using standard units.**

Compare and check

Height	taller / shorter	Length	longer / shorter
Check	line up objects	*Check*	line up objects
Capacity	holds the same, more, less	Weight	same, heavier, lighter
Check	count objects in each	*Check*	hold one object in each hand
	count scoops (rice, water)		use a balance scale

Use a liter as one model, having students judge other containers as holding more or less.

Children tend to think of taller as more. Occasionally, use tall, narrow containers and low, wide containers when comparing capacity so that they experience the tall container holding less than what, to them, appears to be shorter and, therefore, smaller.

Children also think of bigger as heavier. Therefore, sometimes use a small object of greater weight than the bigger object to provide experiences that contradict this thinking. A small, solid metal statue and a balloon filled with air or an empty tissue box, for example.

Measure objects with a variety of informal units, then standard units.

Informal Units	shoe, piece of string, hand span, wrist to elbow, cubes, boxes, jars
	Select a unit used by a culture being studied in history.

Standard Units	Customary	Metric
Length	inches, feet, yards	centimeter
Capacity	cup, pint, quart	liter
Weight	pounds	kilograms*

(*At upper levels the term "mass" may be used along with "weight" when metric grams are involved. However, everyday usage and this guide, for practical purposes, refer to these units as weight only.)

- Students should measure a variety of lengths, including perimeters and areas of polygons for the older children (around age 7). Use square tiles and half tiles for area.

- Teach capacity as filling and packing the container, not tossing things in loosely or filling with less liquid than full. Older children should be able to explain capacity in this way while demonstrating. Have them fill a rectangular solid (shoe box) with cubes to measure capacity in cubic units as part of geometry.

Have students use the following procedure to estimate and measure an object:

1. **Choose a unit.**

   The youngest children may be given something to use. Later, offer a choice of two units, one obviously appropriate, the other very impractical (e.g., a piece of string shorter than the object, one longer than the object). Later, offer two closer choices. After practice with standard units, allow the student to choose from the various standards: inch, feet, yard. This and number five, below, are meant to provide experiences that will later help the student choose and use appropriate units.

2. **Compare that unit to the object using an estimation strategy.**

   Use a reference (cupful of beans) or chunking (putting several units together).

3. **Estimate the measure.**

   Discuss the range of acceptable estimates. Remember, their estimate would be considered accurate if it is within this range. (A range for measuring beans in a jar might be as wide as 250-300 beans. The range for measuring a pencil might only be 5 to 7 inches. Only the actual measurement would be recorded.

4. **Measure the object with the unit, reporting the answer in units.**

   Measure to the degree taught. If inches are being used, the measurement would be to the nearest inch. However, they may want to add "and about a half" or "almost" when going up. (An exact measurement of 3 and 3/4 inches would be written "almost 4 inches.") As they learn about half, connect it to measurements (it looks like half) and include it as part of the recorded answer even though it might not be exact. As they progress with degrees of measurement their recorded answers will become more accurate. At this stage, the emphasis is on developing a sense of capacity, length, and weight.

   For older (age 7) or more able students, have them find out *how many cups are in a pint, and how many pints in a quart.*

And, at least occasionally,

5. Choose another unit, estimate and measure the same object.

    The purpose here is to provide experiences that help children become aware of why one unit would be more appropriate than another. Should the pencil be measured in inches or feet?

When measuring, the use of unit cubes provides a good transition to formal units (an inch cube to find length) as well as remaining useful to find area and capacity.

The Procedure for Measurement

1. Choose the unit. *(A choice may be offered.)*
2. Measure with the unit.
3. Record the units.

While there should be ample opportunities for estimating, there will also be times when it is necessary simply to take a measurement. Older children can compare several line segments that appear close in length by measuring each one with a ruler and then noting the longest or shortest.

Practice   *Learn informal and standard units.*

Allow students to guess (estimate) and check (problem solving).

1. Find something that *measures more than* this object. (E.g., *weighs more, contains more,* or *is longer than.*)

2. Find something that *measures less than* this object. (E.g., *weighs less, contains less,* or *is shorter than.*)

3. Find something that is _____(give measurement). (E.g. *three pounds, one cup, two inches.*)

4. Find as many different objects as you can in (time limit) that are the same (weight, length).

5. Find as many different containers as you can to hold this amount.

6. How much does this hold? (E.g., a *box of cereal, or a canned drink.*) *(capacity)*

7. How tall is this? *(length)*

8. How much does it weigh? (E.g., *a bag of potatoes, a book, or a plate.*)

Use one object for a variety of questions. *(E.g., a box of cereal.)*
- How tall is it? *(length)*
- How large is the front? *(area)*
- How heavy is it? *(weight)*
- How far around is the border? *(perimeter)*
- How much will it hold? *(capacity: how many cups, cubes)*

Activities that combine objectives:

1. **Collect and record information.**

   Have students individually or in a group record the guess and the actual measurement on a chart (or just the actual measurement if estimates are not used). For the youngest children, use pictures to represent objects being measured. Place pictures on the horizontal, the words *guess*, and *check* on the vertical. Students can record the measurement in the correct spaces.

2. **Geometry**

   Have students measure perimeter in centimeters and inches, area with square units, and capacity with unit cubes without using formulas or memorizing terms. *"How far is it around this table?" "How many squares will cover the table top?" "How many cubes will fill this box?"*

   Relate flat squares to area by having students construct polygons with tiles and half tiles.

   Let them use cubes to construct solids to help them become aware of the need for a different unit.

3. **Geography**

   Have students measure routes on maps. *"How far is it to ___?" "Which route is shorter?"*

4. **Physical Education**

   Have students measure long jumps and high jumps, and clock races and rope skipping (counting jumps per minute).

TOPIC:	**TIME**

K-2 OBJECTIVE:	**Identify an event as before or after another.**

K-2 OBJECTIVE:	**Identify an event as longer or shorter than another.**

Emphasis   Develop understanding of time before teaching how to read a clock. Relate the above objectives to real life situations.

Practice

1. Take advantage of everyday activities to ask, *"Which should we do first?"* (before)
   - Wash the dish or scrape off the plate?
   - Color the page or take out a crayon?
   - Put on a coat, go outside, or shovel the snow?
   - Put the seed in the soil or dig a hole?

2. Use two, three, then four picture sequences. These are available in preschool and kindergarten resource guides, or you can make your own. The children would be given the cards out of order and arrange them in sequence.
   Example: *a seed, a seedling, a flower*

3. Take advantage of everyday activities to ask which would take longer. Begin with extreme differences, gradually narrowing the gap. Would it take longer to take a bath or answer the phone? To pour a glass of milk or draw a picture? To play (name a game) or set the table? Questions help build awareness of specific amounts of time.

4. Build awareness of a specific amount of time by using a timer and having the child perform a task (chore or school assignment). When the buzzer sounds, have him notice how much has been completed (hour, minute, and intervals in between).
   - Was there enough time?
   - How much more time do you think you would need?
   - Let's set the timer and find out.

5. Use the timer to make tests: hour, minute, half hour, 15 minutes, 5 minutes, 10 minutes. Students should estimate (guess) and then check by carrying out a timed test.
   - How many times can you bounce the ball in a minute? Start--now. (set a timer)
   - How many triangles can you trace? *(geometry)*
   - How many times can you recite (name a nursery rhyme). *(reading)*
   - How long will it take for this ice cube to melt? *(science)*

6. Name an activity. Offer a choice of two answers. *"Which would be a better estimate?"*
   - Brushing your teeth: a minute or a half hour?
   - Reciting a nursery rhyme: a minute or an hour?
   - Planting a pack of seeds: 5 minutes or an hour?

K-2 OBJECTIVE: Identify days of the week, months of the year, and days in a month.

These are most easily taught with regular calendar activities. Use a large calendar with the numbers in boxes large enough to hold the number and a weather symbol and the days printed neatly. Each day go over the name of the month, the name of the day, and the weather conditions. Have cutouts available to represent sunny (a sun), cloudy (a cloud), rainy (a cloud with rain drops falling), and snowy (a snowflake.) Have a child choose the appropriate symbol. Ask if anyone knows the date. Unless this is the first day of the month, the symbol from the day before should mark yesterday, and they should be able to read the next number to answer the question.

This counts as a chart when planning teaching objectives. Add practice with reasoning and, possibly, probability by making a chart of the weather symbols and tallying the number of each type during the month. Season may enter into discussions if one type of weather was prevalent. Let them look for a pattern if you see one. Several rainy days in a row at the end of the month may suggest letting them predict tomorrow's weather. If there was no snow, or rain, ask for ideas of why that may have been the case. (If this is too difficult, wait until the children are a bit older—8 or 9.)

Practice

1. Practice reading the calendar
   - What day will it be on the tenth?
   - How many days are in the month?
   - How many days are left in this month?
   - What month is next?
   - What day will be the first day of next month?

2. Use ordinals in referring to dates: "Friday is the thirtieth." *Older students (age 8) should be able to use ordinals through thirty-first.*

3. Include practice recognizing numbers before, after, and in between: leave out some dates. Children should decide what number to write in by noticing the numbers before and after.

4. Reciting the months and days of the week will aid retention. Nursery rhymes, *This is the Way We Wash Our Clothes*, for example, would make that more interesting. And at least the first part of the popular rhyme about days in a month would be easy for children to remember and refer to when they are older. *Thirty days has September, April, June, and November; all the rest have thirty-one*—and here's where it gets tricky—*except February, which has 28 except in leap year when it has 29.* Seasons are also taught at this level, usually as part of science or language arts materials.

K-2 OBJECTIVE: **Tell time using a clock: through 5 minute intervals.**

Whether teaching to the hour, half hour, quarter hour or minute, the student reaches mastery only when able to do all of the following:

❑ Read the time when looking at a clock face.

❑ Read the time when looking at numbers and words. "12 o'clock."

❑ Read the time when looking at numbers and the symbol (colon). 12:00 (digital clock) read "12 o'clock."

❑ Fix the hands of a clock to the time given orally.

❑ Fix the hands of a clock to the time given with numbers and words.

❑ Fix the hands of a clock to the time given with numbers and the symbol. E.g., 12:00.

Generally, at age 5 only the hour is taught. *"The long hand points to 12 and we say o'clock."* (Demonstrate.) *"The small hand points to the number we say first."* (Place the small hand on a number 3.) *"This is 3 o'clock."* (Move only the small hand) *"What time does the clock say now?"* Practice from 1 to 12 o'clock.

1. Students should read the hour on a clock.
2. Students should make the hour (move clock hands or draw clock hands) when told the time.
3. Students should write the number next to the word o'clock.
4. Students should write the time without o'clock: 1:00, 2:00, (show a digital clock).
5. Complete all of the above for other times (half hour, quarter hour, to the minute).

Teach 12 o'clock as noon and midnight by discussion.

Practice

Once a child can read the hour, he must become familiar with day and night, since 2 o'clock could either be in the afternoon or while he is asleep. The next step, then, is to relate the time to an event that is a regular part of his life: is it "before noon" (*midnight to noon, referred to as morning*) or "after noon" (*noon to midnight referred to as afternoon, evening, and night*).

1. Have the student set the clock hands to the time of a particular event you mention.
   - What is your bedtime?
   - What time do you start school?
   - What time do you eat lunch?

2. Set the clock hands and have the child tell something he could be doing at that time. Ask for both A.M. and P.M. suggestions.
"What time is this?" "Yes, 2 o'clock. What's something you could do at 2 o'clock in the afternoon?" "What are you doing at 2 o'clock in the morning?"

Relate midnight to noon to A.M. and noon to midnight as P.M. Symbols will be used in grades 3-4.

TOPIC: **GEOMETRY AND SPATIAL SENSE**

Children first learn to see the whole shape, then to analyze the properties of a shape. Later they see relationships between shapes and make simple deductions. Differentiating shapes is necessary in order to recognize letters of the alphabet and is often included in language arts and reading readiness materials.

K-2 OBJECTIVE: **Identify shapes (plane figures): circle, square, triangle, and rectangle.**

K-2 OBJECTIVE: **Identify solids (space figures):   ball (sphere), box (cube), can (cylinder), cone, and pyramid.**

K-2 OBJECTIVE: **Identify sides and corners of a figure.**

K-2 OBJECTIVE: **Draw or make a circle, square, triangle, and rectangle.**

Shapes are plane figures, and solids are space figures. However it is not necessary to introduce these terms to young children until they have had experiences with the concepts. Even then, the more popular labels—shapes and solids—may continue to be used.

Relate the cone to a party hat, ice cream cone, teepee, etc. The other shapes can be pointed out in the items listed above (ball, box, can). Children may be shown pictures of Egyptian pyramids, but should also see a model of that shape as a solid. Be sure the model referred to as a box is a cube (all faces are squares of the same dimensions). Sometimes a *rectangular prism* (looks like a box of tissues) is used during exploratory activities. That could be referred to by its proper name since use and reference would be limited until grades 3 and 4.

Teach solids and shapes.

1. Use manipulatives for initial teaching.

   Once a manipulative is easily recognized, introduce the picture of that shape filled in. When that is recognized, outlines may be used as well.

2. Have students sort and classify to build awareness of shapes.

Provide a model. Have children sort those <u>like</u> the model, those <u>not like</u> the model. The easiest way to do this is to have a set of blocks that differ only in shape.

3. Introduce one shape at a time, always varying the position.

(A triangle can point in any direction and it is still a triangle.) Students must recognize a shape has changed position. In grades 3-4 these changes will be referred to as slides, flips, and turns.

4. Have children find examples of the shape within his surroundings.

circles	clock face, compact disk, plate, end of a flashlight
rectangles	table top, refrigerator door, switch plate, place mat
spheres (balls)	globe, baseball, ping pong ball

5. Have children find examples in pictures.

Check the library for primary level books that teach shapes. They often include clown's with a cone shape hat, seals balancing balls, and so on.

6. Introduce outlines of shapes by having children copy a shape on a geoboard.

The shape being copied could be a block or a picture that is filled in (colored.) The rubber band makes the outline on the geoboard.

7. Provide a variety of activities for practice with shapes.

- Make a picture using shapes. *Paper cutouts, felt shapes on a flannel board.*
- Draw or paint a picture using shapes. *Square house with triangle roof.*
- Make a model of a plane figure with toothpicks, straws, sticks, etc.
- Shape Bingo. Purchase or make your own. Score cards have a shape in each box. A shape card is drawn and a marker placed on the match.

8. Have children identify a shape by touch alone. *(Reach into a bag or wear a blindfold.)*

9. Name a shape. Have the children draw or make it without referring to a model. (Make it on a geoboard, with pattern blocks, by drawing, and so on.)

K-2 OBJECTIVE: **Compare shapes as same or different.**

K-2 OBJECTIVE: **Identify a figure as a shape or solid.**

K-2 Objective: **Identify sides and corners of a figure.**

K-2 Objective: **Associate a drawing with the actual object.**

K-2 Objective: **Identify the inside and outside of a figure.**

K-2 Objective: **Identify symmetry in a figure.**

Analyzing Shapes and Solids

Begin with a few examples that are the same size and color, varying their positions so that the child can discover the attributes (characteristics) of the shape or solid by looking for answers to your leading questions. Include practice with problem solving skills by letting them guess, check, and record information on a chart. If the children are able, they can answer these questions for several models, filling in a chart, rather than examining only one during the lesson.

Shapes
How many sides (edges) does it have?
How many corners are there? (Later, corners will be called vertices.)
Are all the sides the same length?
Does it have symmetry? *(See page 73.)*

Solids
Does it roll? (curved)
Are there flat sides? How many?
What shape are the flat sides? (faces)
Does it have a corner?

 To help students identify the shape of faces of solids, relating it to shapes, have them trace the face, press it into clay (imprint), or press it on an ink pad and print its shape on paper.

Chart Comparisons

A chart can be set up for young children that would only require them to write an "X" to indicate that two shapes share an attribute. Place a model of one shape at the top. Put shapes to be compared to this model in each row. Label columns with attributes.

(See page 74.)

	do not roll	same # of sides	same # of corners	congruent
▲	X	X	X	X
▬	X			
●	X			

Analyzing Data

Students can interpret collected data by comparing shapes 2 at a time. How are they alike? How are they different? The answers should stick to shape attributes (see the questions above) and not refer to size or color. "Rectangles are a lot like squares, except two sides are longer than the other two sides," would be acceptable, "The rectangles are blue and the squares are yellow," would not.

Direct student to look at overall results and draw a conclusion.
"The ball, can, and cone rolled, the box and pyramid didn't." Things with round edges roll. Things with only flat edges don't roll.

Eventually students should be able to recite from memory the number of sides and corners of a specified shape.

Symmetry

Bilateral symmetry means that a center line (an axis) can be drawn and both sides will be exactly alike. The easiest way to test this is to see if you can fold a paper cutout of the shape in half. If the edges of each side touch, the shape has bilateral symmetry. To visualize this, place the fold against a mirror and look at its reflection obliquely (from the side of the mirror). If the shape has bilateral symmetry, the half and its reflection will look like the whole shape. Use the term *symmetry*, not bilateral symmetry, with children.

Practice

Symmetry

1. Fold paper in half. Choose a symmetrical shape, lining up its axis with the paper's fold. Trace the half shape and cut on the pencil line. When opened, the whole shape is revealed in both the cutout and the hole in the paper, demonstrating *symmetry*. (Hearts are especially popular.)

2. Fold a paper. Open it and paint a design on one side of the fold. Before the paint dries, close the paper and press. Open it and notice that an identical design is now on the other side of the fold. (*symmetry*)

Shapes and Solids

3. Playing the game *What Am I?*

   Someone describes a polygon or solid, using number of sides and corners, and any other relevant information. When children learn about angles later, that information can be included. The answer could be given in any of the following ways:
   - Respond verbally. (*"That describes a square."*)
   - Find the described shape on an answer sheet of choices or find an example in the room.
   - Draw the described shape.
   - Make the described shape with rubber bands on a geoboard.

K-2 Objective: **Make congruent figures on a geoboard.**

K-2 Objective: **Match congruent figures.**

Congruent means a shape is exactly the same size and shape as the model. Students often have difficulty finding a shape congruent to the model when their choices are rotated. When using cutouts (paper or felt) the child can physically match the shapes. Put the model on a flannel board or paste it to poster board. Give the child the shape to be checked, have him make a guess, then check by placing it on the model. Let him turn it: now does it match? Are the shapes congruent? Children should become as familiar with the term congruent as they are with the words circle, square and triangle.

Once children are ready for outlines, use a geoboard. They can make a reproduction of the model, then turn the geoboard and observe the shape in a variety of positions.

K-2 Objective: **Make solids using patterns.**

Make a model of a solid with a paper pattern to cut, fold, and glue. This will help children become aware of space inside space figures, which they will later study as volume.

Topic: # FRACTIONS

K-2 Objective: **Understand fractions as a whole and equal parts of a whole for a region.**

K-2 Objective: **Understand fractions as a whole and equal parts of a whole for a group.**

Background Children must recognize a whole and the parts that make up that whole. Then they should be able to identify the whole even when a part is missing. This concept is taught at the preschool and kindergarten level, and is a skill that precedes recognition of fractions—which are **equal** parts of a whole. If this is lacking:

Teach the concept.

1. Use familiar objects and help the child recognize the parts and their functions.
   - *His body*   He can experiment to find out which parts are especially important to a specified task: *buttoning his shirt, throwing a ball, asking for a drink.*
   - *Telephone*   buttons or dial to call, a receiver to speak and listen.
   - *Bicycle*   wheels to go, a seat for sitting, handle bars to hold and steer.

2. Next, show pictures of an object with a part missing. The child should be able to identify what is missing: a bird without a leg, a phone without a dial, a clock without hands.

3. Progress to jigsaw puzzles which require fitting several pieces to form a complete picture. Encourage the child to use visual clues rather than randomly trying each piece.

   Cutouts of numbers could be used along with learning numerals. Cut a paper or cardboard numeral into several pieces and have the child put it together.

   Parquetry blocks can be used to build designs. The pieces are then seen as pieces in a puzzle, parts of a whole. By using the design cards, children also practice matching shapes.

4. Remove a piece from a puzzle and ask what is missing. If the child doesn't know, have him choose the piece from among several incorrect choices.

 Once children are ready for fractions begin with halves, then teach thirds and fourths.

K-2 OBJECTIVE: **Understand parts of a whole as halves, thirds, fourths.**

K-2 OBJECTIVE: **Find equal parts of a whole.**

K-2 OBJECTIVE: **Identify parts of a group (set) as halves, thirds, fourths.**

K-2 OBJECTIVE: **Divide a group of objects (set) into halves, thirds, fourths.**

Teach equal parts of a region.
Use fraction pieces—tiles, blocks, and/or bars divided into equal parts.

1. Dividing a whole into two equal parts may be practiced as part of symmetry first. By folding, they can check equality by matching sides. They can also combine identical shapes to make a whole:

   - Two identical triangles fitted together to make a square.
   - Two identical squares arranged to make a rectangle.
   - Two right triangles to make one larger triangle.
   - Two rectangles to make a larger rectangle.

2. Have students combine two identical blocks or cutouts to make a whole. Parts can be placed on top of each other to be certain they are congruent (parquetry blocks, geometric shape blocks). Once students understand the necessity of equal parts a geoboard can be used.

3. The child should be able to look at a shape divided into various pieces and decide if it illustrates "halves" or not. It may be helpful at first to provide 2 or three choices of shapes divided into two pieces, but only one with two equal pieces.

4. Have students find $\frac{1}{2}$. That is, one of two equal pieces.

5. Show the students the written symbol for one half. $\frac{1}{2}$
    Explain that the bottom number (denominator) tells how many pieces are in the whole and the top number (numerator) tells how many pieces we want to use. Continue this process of identification using pictures with $\frac{1}{2}$ shaded for the student to identify.

6. Follow the same procedure (from #2 on) to teach thirds and fourths as children are ready. (Generally at about age six.) Practice with pictures and shaded regions would include identification of $\frac{1}{3}, \frac{2}{3}, \frac{1}{4}, \frac{2}{4}, \frac{3}{4}$.

7. For children that grasp these activities, offer pictures of the following shaded amounts for identification. $\frac{1}{5}, \frac{1}{6}, \frac{1}{7}, \frac{1}{8}, \frac{1}{9}, \frac{1}{10}$.

Teach equal parts of a group.

This can also be included in teaching sets, counting, adding, and division.

1. Begin with small sets of an even number so that they can be divided into two equal groups without anything left over.

    "Here are 6 blocks. Can you divide these so that you and I each have the same amount?" The child would divide by giving one to you, one to himself and so on until there are no more blocks.

    "Do we each have the same amount?" The child can line up the two groups side by side (one-to-one correspondence) to check..

    "We started out with one set of 6 blocks. Now you have half of them and I have half of them."

Continue practicing with a variety of objects and sets of various quantities until the child can take any set and divide it into halves on his own. *"Here are 12 blocks, can you divide this set into halves?" "Here are 6 beans, can you give me half?"*

2. Given two or three sets divided in different ways, the child should be able to choose the set divided into halves. Follow the same procedure for teaching thirds and fourths when the children are able (often at about age six).

GRADES 3 – 4 OBJECTIVES

EMPHASIZE
Procedures for basic operations.
Reasoning to solve problems.

PROVIDE OPPORTUNITIES
To use calculators.
To use computers.

INVOLVE STUDENTS IN
Active participation.
Making and checking predictions.

 Items introduced at this level are in italics.

PROBLEM SOLVING

❑ **Solve various types of problems.**

- **Reasoning**:
  - Classify.
  - Compare.
  - Find patterns.

- **Computation:**
  - Add.
  - Subtract.
  - Multiply.
  - *Divide.*

- **Collect, Record, Analyze Information:**
  - Pictograph.
  - Bar graph.

- **Word Problems:**
  - Choose the operation.
  - Solve one- and two-step problems.

❑ **Understand how to solve one- and two-step problems.**

1. Understand what the problem is asking.
   What does it require: an exact answer, an estimation, collecting information?
2. Decide which information to use.
3. Make and carry out an appropriate plan.
4. Check the answer.

❑ **Use problem solving strategies.**

- **Solve problems mentally.**
  - Count on or back to find sums and differences.
  - Compare numbers.
  - Use a pattern.
  - Use properties to find sums and products.

- **Estimate.**
  - Front-end estimation.
  - Chunking (unitizing).
  - Using rounded or approximate numbers.

- **Use pencil and paper.**
  - Draw a picture to define the problem.
  - Write a number sentence.
  - *Use a formula.*
  - Carry out an operation (add, subtract, multiply, *divide*).

- **Use a calculator.**
  - Compute whole numbers, *decimals, fractions.*

- **Use a computer.**
  - Use software.
  - *Learn programming skills.*

PROBABILITY AND STATISTICS

❑ **Find the probability of an event occurring *and not occurring.***

❑ ***Determine the range, average, median, and mode.***

WHOLE NUMBER CONCEPTS AND COMPUTATION

❑ **Count by: 2, 5, 10, *100.***
   Count by other numbers as an aid to multiplication until facts are memorized.

❑ **Use place value.**

   - Identify place value *through million.*
   - Read and write numbers from one to one million: 0-99; 100-999; *1,000 - 9,999; 10,000-99,999; 100,000 –999,999 and 1,000,000.*
   - Identify the number before, after, and in between.
   - Compare numbers from *1 - 1,000,000:* with words and symbols.

- Round numbers to the nearest 10, *100, 1,000.*

❑ **ADDITION**

Sums less than one million.

- **Understand concepts.**
  - Identify and use addition properties: associative, commutative, zero.
  - Check work by adding in reverse order.
  - Estimate sums using rounding and front-end strategies.

- **Solve vertical and horizontal computation problems.**
  - Mentally add: 1 - 20 to a number less than 10.
  - *Mentally add three single-digit numbers.*
  - Find the missing addend (0-9) in a problem of up to 3 addends.
  - Fill in missing numbers in *3-digit addends* and sums: 25?+ 5?7 = 875.
  - Three single-digit numbers with parentheses to indicate which to add first.
  - Two or more single-digit numbers.
  - Two-digit and 1-, 2-, 3-digit numbers without and with renaming.
  - *Three-digit and four-digit numbers without and with renaming.*
  - *Add columns of four-digit numbers.*

- **Memorize addition facts with sums through 18.**

❑ **SUBTRACTION**

Differences less than one million.

- **Understand concepts.**
  - Check answers using addition.
  - Relate addition and subtraction facts.
  - Estimate differences.

- **Solve vertical and horizontal computation problems.**
  - Review subtraction of 2 numbers whose sums would be 18 or less.
  - 1- or 2-digit number from a 2-digit number without/with renaming.
  - *1-, 2-, and 3-digit numbers from 3- and 4- digit numbers without/with renaming.*
  - *1-, 2-, 3-, 4-, or 5-digit number from a 5-digit number.*

- **Memorize subtraction facts with differences through 18.**

❏ **MULIPLICATION**

Multiply by a few numbers, then divide with those same numbers.

- **Understand concepts.**
  - Relate multiplication and division as inverse operations.
  - Review and use the commutative property.
  - *Find multiples of a number.*
  - *Mentally multiply by multiples of 10.*
  - *Estimate products by rounding.*
  - *Determine common multiples (grade 4).*

- *Memorize basic facts 0-9 times 0-9.*

- **Solve computation problems.**
  - 1-digit through *4-digit numbers* by 2, 3, 4; then by 5, 6, 7; then by 8, 9, 0, 1.
  - *Multiply money, less than ten dollars, by a one-digit number.*
  - *Multiply a 1-digit number and then a 2-digit number by 10, 100, 1,000.*

  Grade 4
  - *2- and 3-digit numbers by 2-digit numbers (10 - 99) without/with renaming.*
  - *Multiply money, less than ten dollars, by a two-digit number.*
  - *Multiply 3-digit and 4-digit factors without/with renaming.*

❏ **DIVISION**

- **Understand concepts.**
  - Identify the relationship of division to multiplication.

- **Solve computation problems.**
  - *Divide by 2 - 5; 6 - 9; 10 - 99   with one- and two-digit quotients.*
  - *1- and 2-digit numbers by a 1- digit divisor, without, with remainder.*

  Grade 4
  - *3- and 4-digit by 1-digit without and with remainder: quotients to 3-digits.*
  - *Divide by 10, 100, 1,000 without, then with a remainder.*
  - *2- and 3-digit by 2-digit: one- and two-digit quotients.*

FRACTIONS

❏ **Understand concepts.**

- *Match a written fraction to a shaded region.*
- *Match a written fraction to a fractional part of a group.*
- *Explain meaning of terms numerator and denominator.*
- *Compare and order like fractions.*
- *Write equivalent fractions.*

- *Identify fractions as mixed numbers.*
- *Write fractions in lowest terms (simplify).*
- ***Grade 4:*** *Compare and order unlike fractions.*

❑ **Solve computation problems.**

- *Add and subtract fractions with like, and unlike denominators.*
- *Add fractions and mixed numbers with the same denominators.*
- *Convert fractions and mixed numbers to a decimal.*

ROMAN NUMERALS

❑ ***Identify values of Roman numerals: I V X L***

❑ ***Convert Roman numeral combinations to standard notation and vice versa.*** *(VI = 6; 11 = XI)*

DECIMALS

Use models to aid in understanding concepts.

❑ **Understand concepts.**

- *Using a block of 100 squares, identify shaded tenths, hundredths.*
- *Relate decimals to fractions: tenths, hundredths.*
- *Identify place value to tenths, then hundredths.*
- *Compare two decimals with place value through tenths, then hundredths.*
- *Order decimals least to greatest.*
- *Round decimals to the nearest whole number.*

❑ **Solve computation problems.**

- *Estimate sums, differences, and add and subtract decimals—same place value.*
- *Estimate sums, differences, and add and subtract decimals—different place value.*

Do all of the above with tenths *(grade 3)* **before hundredths are introduced.**

MONEY

❑ **Recognize, count money, and make change** *up to $20.00.*

❑ **Add and subtract** *dollars.*

❑ ***Multiply and divide money less than $10.00 by a one-digit number.***

❑ **Solve one- and two-step word problems requiring addition or subtraction of money.**

TIME

❑ **Understand concepts.**

- Tell whether a time is before or after another time.
- *Identify A.M. and P.M.*
- *Recognize century, B.C. and A.D.*
- *Recognize time zones.*
- *Read a schedule.*

❑ **Solve computation problems.**

- *Find elapsed time.*
- Solve word problems using time: clock, calendar.
- *Tell time to the minute.*

GEOMETRY

❑ **Identify lines:**

- *Line segment.*
- *Ray.*
- *Intersecting lines.*
- *Parallel lines.*
- *Perpendicular lines.*

❑ **Identify shapes (plane figures).**

- Identify a figure as open or closed.
- *Identify* circles, squares, rectangles, *polygons, quadrilaterals, trapezoids, and parallelograms.*
- *Identify right, isosceles, and equilateral triangles.*
- Identify the number of angles, faces, edges, and vertices.
- Find a line of symmetry.
- *Identify a slide, flip, and turn of a figure,* congruent figures, and *similar* figures.
- *Identify parts of a circle: center point, diameter, and radius.*

❑ **Identify angles.**

- *Identify a right angle.*
- *Identify angles as greater or less than a right angle.*

❑ **Solve computation problems.**

- Determine the perimeter of a figure.
- *Determine the area of a figure in square units, including finding it with multiplication.*
- *Determine the volume of a rectangular prism in cubic units using a formula.*
- *Solve problems involving perimeter, area, and volume.*

MEASUREMENT

❑ *Recognize symbols and abbreviations for units, and the value of metric prefixes.*

❑ *Convert from smaller to larger measurements within a system (e.g., feet to miles, cups to quarts).*

❑ *Choose the appropriate unit for measuring when told what is to be measured.*

❑ *Estimate an answer using the appropriate measure in a situation where no hint is given.* (*How much water will this bucket hold?*)

❑ *Add and subtract measures.*

❑ **Estimate, then measure length, capacity, temperature, weight.**

- **Length**
  - *to the fractional part of an inch.*
  - inch, foot, yard, *mile.*
  - centimeter, *meter, kilometer.*

- **Capacity (liquid volume)**
  - fluid ounce, cup, pint, quart, *gallon.*
  - *milliliter,* liter.

- **Weight**
  - *ounce,* pound.
  - *gram,* kilogram.
  - *Read a scale.*

- **Temperature**
  - Associate with appropriate dress.
  - Read a thermometer: Celsius, Fahrenheit.

TOPIC: **PROBLEM SOLVING**

Types of Problems

Vary the types of problems students solve. Include the following:

❑ **Reasoning**
Classify, compare, look for patterns, and use deductive and inductive logic.

⇒ Use some materials that have reasoning as the primary objectives (logic workbooks such as *Mindbenders*). Continue with visual patterns described in *Teaching K-2*, page 36. *(Check "Supplies," pages 13-14, for logic workbooks.)*

⇒ Have students look for number relationships—how does a change in one quantity affect the other?

⇒ Reinforce number concepts while providing practice classifying with the following pattern:

Find the *(define set to choose from: odd, even, whole number, decimal)* less than *(give number or expression)* and more than *(give number or expression)* that are [or are not] *(terms for solution set).*

"Find the odd numbers less than 3x7 and more than 4-1 that are divisible by 3 without a remainder."

Or list limits	The numbers are	*less than (21)*	*greater than (3)*
		not even	*divisible by 3*

The description limits the choices for the solution set. While he works, the student can look for a pattern. In the example above, he would try dividing numbers 5, 7, 9, 11, 13, 15, 17, and 19 by 3. Those that have no remainder would be listed in brackets as the solution set: {9, 15} The pattern he could notice: *The numbers divisible by 3 are also multiples of 3.*

❑ **Computation**
Practice with procedures. Memorize facts to help speed and accuracy.

Work toward a thorough understanding of procedures for adding, subtracting, multiplying and dividing whole numbers.

❑   **Collect, Record, Analyze Information**

Use pictographs and bar graphs.
The teacher makes the chart. The students add the data and discuss the meaning.

Bar Graph

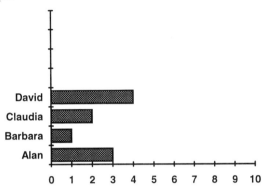

Pictograph

Name	Telephones at home
Alan	☎ ☎ ☎
Barbara	☎
Claudia	☎ ☎
David	☎ ☎ ☎ ☎

Analyzing Data

How many phones does *Alan* have?   Who has more than *one* phone?
Who has an *even number* of phones?   Who has the most phones? fewest?
What is the average number of phones?   Who has less (more) than average?
Order the number of phones: least to greatest   What is the range? mode? median?

❑   **Word Problems**

Word problems combine reasoning and calculation. Make up problems, some of which use real life situations, that require the student to decide whether to add, subtract, multiply or divide. Include problems that require two steps, which can be the same operation, or different operations. These should be scattered throughout the curriculum to provide application of computation skills being taught.

One-Step Patterns
There are 15 pencils in the box. How many in 6 boxes?
There are 12 kittens in the cage and 5 cages in the store.
How many kittens are in the store?

Two-Step Patterns

There are 23 cats entered in each contest. There are 9 contests scheduled each week. How many cat entries are in contests over a 6 week period?

There are 12 windowpanes in each window. There are 5 windows in each room. How many windowpanes are in 6 rooms?

3-4 OBJECTIVE: **Solve problems requiring one or two steps.**

Students should acquire the habit of asking themselves questions that will help them reason through a problem. At the K-2 level, teacher questions were suggested. The following steps and questions can be used at all age levels, as needed.

1. What is the problem? *(Understand the problem.)*
    Do I understand all the words? (If not, ask for help.)
    Do I need to give an <u>exact</u> answer or an estimate (<u>about</u> how many)?
    Do I have to collect information or is everything here?

2. Which information should I use?
    Is there enough information to solve the problem?
    If there is more information than necessary, which is important?

3. What should I do to solve it? *(Make a plan.)*
    Draw a picture if it will help you visualize the problem.
    Write a number sentence for the problem.
    If you are to estimate, think of the best strategy to use.
    Is there a pattern that will make finding the answer easier?

4. Do the work. *(Carry out the plan.)*
    Decide whether to do this mentally, with a calculator, or using pencil and paper.
    Carry out the operation.

5. Check your answer.
    Is it reasonable? *(Check mentally using estimation.)*
    Check your calculation with a standard procedure:

If an exact answer is required, and your answer looks reasonable—you think you carried out the correct operation with the right numbers—check the calculation with standard checking procedures. (Add in reverse order. Add the difference to the number subtracted.)

      Deciding whether to estimate: Does the problem ask "about how many?" If so, you can use estimation strategies to answer the question.

3-4 OBJECTIVE: **Learn problem solving strategies.**

(Refer also to pages 36-39.)

❑   **Patterns**

Continue looking for visual patterns described in K-2, *("What's next?")* and number patterns suggested as strategies for teaching addition and subtraction facts. Besides the patterns mentioned throughout this guide (within specific topics), look for materials that suggest entertaining activities involving patterns. *Family Math* includes one with palindromes—numbers that read the same backward and forward such as 2442.

❑   **Use properties to find sums and products by arranging the numbers for easier calculation.**

Commutative property   Two numbers can be added or multiplied in any
$a + b = b + a$ $a \times b = b \times a$ order without affecting their sum or product.

Associative property   The order in which three or more numbers are
$(a + b) + c = a + (b + c)$ grouped can be changed without affecting their
$(a \times b) \times c = a \times (b \times c)$ sum or product.

Add $49 + 25 + 1 + 20$ *Think* $49 + 1$ is 50; $50 + 25$ is 75; and 20 more: 75, 85, **95**.

Multiply $2 \times 6 \times 5$ *Think* 2×5 is 10; 10×6 is **60**.

❑   **Estimation Strategies**

Use estimation when developing awareness of quantities. Work toward development of the ability to recognize situations where estimation is appropriate, to choose which unit to use, and to decide whether the answer is reasonable.

❑   **Estimate with rounded or approximate numbers.**

Students choose numbers that are easy to work in giving an estimate for addition, subtraction, multiplication and division. 23 plus 54: "23 is almost 25 and 54 is near 50. 25 plus 50 is 75, so the answer is about 75." Students should be able to tell if their estimation is high or low depending on whether they substituted numbers greater or less than the original numbers.

To add a series of numbers, look for easy facts, like pairs, or sums of ten: 23 + 26 + 19 might be added this way: "26 is almost 27; Add 23 and 27—7+3 is **10** and 20 + 20 is **40**, so, 23 + 27 is 50; 19 is almost 20, so, 50 + 20 is 70." If this method was used to mentally check whether or not a calculated answer was reasonable, they now know the exact answer (68) should be close to 70.

Look at the divisor, then at the dividend. How could the dividend be changed to be divided evenly: that is, so there won't be a remainder. Mentally divide. The answer will be an estimate. For example: 20 divided by 7: 3 sevens are 21, so the estimate is 3—slightly higher than an exact answer. To use this technique, children should know basic multiplication facts, place value, and how to divide to find exact answers.

TOPIC: **PROBABILITY AND STATISTICS**

3-4 OBJECTIVE: **Find the probability of an event occurring and not occurring.**

Continue with activities discussed in *Teaching K-2*, pages 41-42, but have students write the probability.

Help children understand the probability of an event <u>not</u> occurring:

If using a spinner and 4 colors (the circle must be divided into equal pieces) ask, *"What is the probability (or chance) of the spinner stopping at yellow (i.e., name a color on the circle)?"* The response would be to say, "One out of four," and to write ¼. Then ask, *"What is the probability that it won't stop at yellow (i.e., name the same color)?"* The response would be 3 out of 4, written ¾. *(The student may need to think it through. "There are 4 colors, 1 is yellow, 3 are not, so there are three chances out of the four that it won't be yellow.")*

If you have 8 blocks in a box—2 blue, 3 yellow, 3 red, ask, *"What is the probability that you won't remove a red block (assuming you can't see into the box)."* *"There are a total of 8 chances, and 5 blocks are not red, so there are 5 out of 8 chances that you will not choose a red block."*

3-4 OBJECTIVE: **Find the range, average (mean), median and mode.**

At this age, activities with statistics involve reading graphs and tables. Since children should become familiar with circle graphs, bar graphs, line graphs, and tables, look for opportunities to use these forms to provide the information for calculating range, average, and/or mode.

Range **The range of a group of numbers is found by <u>subtracting</u> the smallest number (least value) from the largest number (greatest value).**

Data: 2, 6, 9, 13   Calculate: 13 - 2   Range: 11

Children should have been introduced to the idea of range in K-2 when helping decide a range of acceptable answers for an estimate. Continue to use range in this way.

Average   <u>Add</u> all the numbers and <u>divide</u> by the number of addends to find the average of a set of numbers.

Find the average correct on 2 months of spelling tests.

Scores   10, 13, 9, 15, 11, 13, 14, 13

Calculate   10 + 13 + 9 + 15 + 11 + 13 + 14 + 13 = 98
             98 divided by 8 scores = 12 ¼

Average   12 ¼

The range of scores would be 5 points: 15 - 10 = 5

Median   **Arrange data in numerical order, least to greatest. The number in the middle is the median.** If two numbers are in the middle, add them together and divide by two.

Scores   9, 10, 11, <u>13, 13,</u> 13, 14, 15

<u>Median</u> = 13   13 + 13 = 26; 26 ÷2 = 13

Scores   2, 4, <u>5,</u> 7, 13

<u>Median</u> = 5   5 is in the center.

Students should try to find a pattern for finding one or two numbers in the center. *(An odd number of scores will have one number in the center. An even number of scores will have two center numbers.)*

Mode   **The number in a set that occurs most often.**

Scores   10, 13, 9, 15, 11, 13, 14, 13 *(three 13's)*   <u>Mode</u> = 13

There are two popular ways to determine mode.

1. Make a tally chart.
   Count the tallies.

9	10	11	13	14	15
I	I	I	III	I	I

2. List the numbers from least to greatest.
   Find the number listed the most.

   9 10 11 13 13 13 14 15   *There are three thirteens.*

Use manipulatives if children have difficulty.

NUMBER CONCEPTS AND COMPUTATION

Teaching Tips:

1. Introduce the concept with manipulatives and/or illustrations.
2. Let the students figure things out by asking them leading questions as often as possible.
3. Provide practice with manipulatives and/or illustrations using a few simple numbers before moving on to greater numbers and/or a wider range of numbers.
4. Encourage memorization of concepts, facts, formulas and procedures (algorithms).
5. Provide practice without manipulatives or illustrations. (The process must become automatic.)
6. Provide review of previously learned material. (Retention requires use.)
7. Build speed in computation while maintaining accuracy.

PLACE VALUE

3-4 OBJECTIVE: **Read and write numbers through one million.**

Refer to pages 50-52 in *Teaching K-2* for place value through the hundreds. Then provide a chart that includes thousands. Have students use place value manipulatives to rename 10 hundred flat squares with a thousand block

thousands	hundreds	tens	ones
3	1	4	7

Students should

1. Look at blocks representing a number in the thousands and record that number on the chart. *Set out blocks in the same order as the chart: thousands, hundreds, tens, ones.*

2. Look at a number on the chart and make it with the place value blocks.

3. Write what has been recorded on the chart as a number on its own: 3147

4. Write numbers in *expanded notation:* 3000 + 100 + 40 + 7

5. Read a number using place value words and write it in standard form *(standard notation).*   Read: 3 thousands 1 hundred 4 tens 7 ones Write: 3,147

6. Write a number in standard form that is given orally, or written as it would be spoken: *"three thousand, one hundred and forty-seven."*

Once students are comfortable with place value through the thousands, introduce ten thousands and hundred thousands. Use only charts unless children appear confused and need to return to place value manipulatives for understanding. For students that perform better by acting out rather than reading and writing, use number cards and make a pocket under each place value to hold them.

thousands			ones		
hundreds	tens	ones	hundreds	tens	ones
5	2	0	3	6	7

Write a number in each place, then write the standard form of that number: 520,367
Point out the comma to set apart the thousands. Tell the students how to read the number.
This is five hundred and twenty <u>thousand</u>, three hundred and sixty-seven."

As students are able, introduce the next place to the left as one million, showing them ten millions, and hundred millions so that they can see the pattern. Explain that a comma separates millions from thousands, and thousands from ones. Eventually they'll follow the rule of counting from right to left and placing a comma after every three places. For now, they should see how the comma helps us read and interpret a number.

Students should be able to:

1. Write a number with numerals when it is dictated. (E.g., say, *"one hundred and five."* The student would write 105.)

2. Look at a number written with numerals and write it in words—as it would be spoken. E.g., look at 200,060 and write *two hundred thousand and sixty.*

3. Give the value of any digit in a six place number.
    E.g., *"What is the value of the 5 in 135,789?"* The student would say, *"Five is 5 thousand"* or write 5,000.

4. <u>Write</u> the number for their estimate. E.g., the number of letters on a cereal box.

3-4 OBJECTIVE: **Compare and order numbers through one million.**

Compare   Students should read and use symbols for greater than >, less than <, and equal to (=), placing the symbol correctly between two numbers. 2351 < 3169   Read *"two thousand, three hundred and fifty-one <u>is less than</u> three thousand, one hundred and sixty-nine.*

Numbers can be compared first by making and then comparing sets. Have them use place value manipulatives, arranging them correctly, largest place value first. Teach them to look at the bars of greatest value first. Practice should lead them to the conclusion that it is not necessary to count, but only to note the first place of greatest value where the quantities are different. The way those quantities compare will be true of the numbers. With this understanding, they can simply look at the numbers, comparing digits left to right.

Compare   3323   to   3349

Using manipulatives   The same number of thousand blocks and hundred blocks are in each set. Compare the tens. One set has two and the other four. The set with four tens would be the greater number. They would now place the symbol to open to the greatest number: 3323 < 3349 and read the comparison: *"three thousand three-hundred and twenty three is less than three thousand three hundred and forty-nine."*

Mentally   3 3 2 3   Check the far left: *same*
                  3 3 4 9   Check the next place to the right: *same*
                             Check the next place to the right (tens): *different.*
                             Which is greater? 4 is greater than 2.
                             Therefore, 3349 is greater than 3323.

Order

To arrange numbers least to greatest, follow the same procedure above, comparing two numbers at a time. Student should be able to write numbers before, after, and in between other numbers.

3-4 OBJECTIVE: **Round numbers to the nearest 10, 100, 1,000.**
Rounding numbers is used as an estimation strategy.

To the nearest ten   Look at the ones place. If the digit is 5 or more, count it as a ten (round up). If the digit is 4 or less, count it as nothing (round down).

Learning with a number line

Five is half way between 1 and 10, 25 is half way between 20 and 30, and so on. The numbers to the right of the midway point are nearer to the higher number. Sixteen is nearer to 20. Numbers to the left of the midway point are nearer to the lesser number. 34 is nearer to 30.

Looking at a number

135   Look at the 5. Count it as a ten. Look at the tens. You have 3 already, and now have one more. Rounded to the nearest ten, 135 would be 140.

133   Look at the 3. Count it as nothing. That won't change the tens: 133 would be 130.

Using manipulatives (Some children need *hands-on* more often than others.)

Write down the number. Make a model of it with place value manipulatives. Replace five or more ones with a ten bar. If there are less than five ones, remove them. Write down the new number represented by the manipulatives. That is the rounded number.

To the nearest hundred   Look at the tens place. If the digit is 5 or more, count the tens and ones as a hundred. If the digit is 4 or less, count the tens and ones as nothing.

Using a number line

Use 50 as the midway point between hundreds: 100 - 150 - 200 - 250 - 300. Numbers to the right of the 50 are nearer to the next hundred (round up). Numbers to the left are nearer to the lesser hundred (round down): 233 is nearer 200. 278 is nearer 300.

Looking at the number

2561   Look at the 6. It's more than five, so the 61 will be considered another hundred. Add it to the 5 hundreds. The number would now read 2600.

2510   Look at the 1. It's less than five, so throw away the ten. The number would now read 2500.

To the nearest thousand   Look at the digit in the hundred's place. If it is 5 or more, consider it and the numbers after it to make up a thousand. If it's less than 5, consider it and the number after it as zero.

Using a number line

500 is the midway point. At 500 and above, round up to the next thousand. At anything less than the midway point, round down to the lesser thousand. 2501 would be rounded to 3000 because it is to the right of the midway point (2500).

Looking at the number

3749   7 is greater than 5, so the 749 is considered another thousand. There were 3 thousand. One more is added. The result is 4000.

3489   4 is less than 5, so the 489 is thrown away. That leaves 3,000.

ADDITION

Use the terms *addend, plus, equals,* and *sum,* i.e., addend (5) plus (+) addend (6) equals (=) sum (11).

3-4 OBJECTIVE: **Identify and use the associative, commutative, and zero properties of addition.**

Discovering these properties was discussed in *Teaching K-2,* page 53. Now the properties are referred to by name and used more frequently.

Commutative Property $a + b = b + a$ $3 + 5 = 5 + 3$
Two numbers can be added in any order without affecting the sum.

Associative Property $(a + b) + c = a + (b + c)$ $(3 + 5) + 2 = 3 + (5 + 2)$
The order in which three or more numbers are grouped can be changed without affecting their sum. (Add numbers in parentheses first.)

Zero Property of Addition $a + 0 = a$ $3 + 0 = 3$
The sum of any number and zero is that number.

3-4 OBJECTIVE: **Estimate sums using rounding and front-end strategy.**

Rounding $12 + 27 + 9$ Think: $10 + 30 + 10$ The answer is about 50.

Front-end   1 ten and 2 tens is 30, $7 + 2$ is about 10 and 9 is about ten,
                   $30 + 10 + 10 = 50$

3-4 OBJECTIVE: **Solve problems written vertically and horizontally.**

3-4 OBJECTIVE: **Mentally add 1-20 to a number less than 10. Mentally add three single-digit numbers.**

Sometimes horizontal problems use parentheses to indicate which numbers to add first. If not, they are generally added left to right. In a vertical problem, the general procedure is to add top to bottom and check adding bottom to top. However, children should put the associate and commutative properties to use to *add columns more quickly by looking for numbers that are easily added (compatible numbers): facts they know, doubles, pairs that make ten.*

```
  9     Mentally add:  9 + 1 makes 10, and 5 more is 15.
  5
+ 1
```

3-4 OBJECTIVE: **Find the missing addend in a problem of up to 3 addends where addends are each less than 10.**

This also draws on knowledge of addition and subtraction facts. Practice with those facts (work toward memorization) will make these problems easier, and allow children to solve them mentally.

$2 + 5 + ? = 10$ Children add the two known addends and ask themselves "7 plus what is 10?" If they know the addition facts, or just those that have the pattern of adding up to 10, they know that the missing number is three.

$9 + ? + 5 = 15$ Here they could add the 9 and 5 then ask 14 plus what is 15 to find the missing one. But, some children may see that 10 and 5 make fifteen and they have the five, and almost a ten, arriving at one by recognizing that 9 + 1 is 10. Allow for variety in approach to a problem as long as it is logical and doesn't violate any rules of mathematics.

3-4 OBJECTIVE: **Fill in missing numbers in 3-digit addends and sums.**

```
  4 ? 3
+ ? 5 2
  7 2 ?
```
These types of problems reinforce addition facts and the procedure for adding.

3-4 OBJECTIVE: **Add up to 3- and 4-digit numbers without and with regrouping (renaming).**

Review   Sums involving addition facts, three single-digit addends, two-digit numbers without and with regrouping (also called "carrying").

Introduce   3- and 4-digit numbers.
Addition of columns of three numbers.
Missing addends.

Practice

Coordinate with numbers learned in place value lessons. First assign problems that do not require regrouping. Allow students to use place value manipulatives as aids.

 Unless the student can add a horizontal problem mentally, he should write it vertically, being careful to line up numbers according to place value. Neat work is especially important for accuracy. Students may find it helpful to write problems on graph paper—one numeral per box.

Problem   1257 + 837   Write   1257
                                        + 837

Procedure for addition

Step 1   Add the ones

Step 2   Write the sum below the ones column.

Step 3   Add the tens.

Step 4   Write the sum below the tens column.

Continue this procedure for the hundreds column, then the thousands and so on.

Procedure for addition with renaming
Instructions for using manipulatives are in italics.

Step 1   Add ones. When there are ten or more, trade for tens. *Place these tens with the other tens.* Write the number of tens you traded above the other numbers in the tens column.

Step 2   Write the number of <u>ones left</u> in the answer space under the ones column.

Step 3   Add all tens. If there are more than ten, trade each group of ten tens for one hundred. *Place the hundreds with the other hundreds.* Write the number of hundreds you traded above the other numbers in the hundreds column.

Step 4   Write the number of <u>tens left</u> in the answer space below the tens column.

Step 5   Add all hundreds. Trade each group of ten hundreds for one thousand. *Place with other thousands.* Write the number of thousands you traded above the other thousands.

```
   1
 1257        1. Add 7 + 9:  16 = 1 ten 6 ones.
+ 849        2. Write 1 above the tens column, and 6 below the ones column.
    6


  11
 1257        3. Add 1 + 5 + 4:  10 = 1 set of ten tens.
+ 849        4. Write 1 above the hundreds column, and 0 below the tens column.
   06


 111
 1257        5. Add 1 + 2 + 8:  11 = 1 set of 10 hundreds (1 thousand), 1 hundred.
+ 849        6. Write 1 above the thousands, 1 below hundreds.
 2106        7. Add 1 + 1 and write 2 below the thousands.
```

Practice

1. Have students experiment with single-digit addends to reason through the following:
    - What would happen to the sum if the addends were doubled? *The sum is doubled.*
    - If zero was included as an addend? *There is no change.*
    - If the addends were increased by one? *Count the number of addends, add that number to the sum.   E.g., 4 + 5 + 2 = 11. There are 3 addends, so 5 + 6 + 3 should equal 3 more than 11.*

2. Have students practice addition facts by listing facts with the same sum together.

☞   Sums of 10, are used frequently in adding mentally:

1 + 9	2 + 8	3 + 7	4 + 6	5 + 5	6 + 4	7 + 3	8 + 2	9 + 1

SUBTRACTION

Use the terms minuend, minus, subtrahend, equals, and difference, i.e. minuend (9) minus (-) subtrahend (4) equals (=) difference (5).

3-4 OBJECTIVE: **Subtract up to a 5-digit number from a 5-digit number, without and with renaming.**

Review   Subtraction facts and two-digit numbers without and with regrouping. *(Refer to pages 55-57.)*

Introduce   Problems with larger numbers in coordination with those used in place value lessons and addition problems.

Practice   Allow students to use place value manipulatives as aids while solving problems.

Reasoning   Why must the ones be subtracted first?

It helps to remember a procedure if the reasoning is clear. *When regrouping is involved in addition you wouldn't know if there were any extra tens unless you had already added the ones. In subtraction you wouldn't know if the tens or hundreds were changed (renamed) unless you subtracted the ones.*

Renaming: step-by-step

$$
\begin{array}{r}
435 \\
-189 \\
\hline
\end{array}
\qquad
\begin{array}{r}
{\scriptstyle 2\ 15} \\
4\cancel{3}\cancel{5} \\
-189 \\
\hline
6
\end{array}
\qquad
\begin{array}{r}
{\scriptstyle 3\ 12\ 15} \\
\cancel{4}\cancel{3}\cancel{5} \\
-189 \\
\hline
246
\end{array}
$$

 Writing on a chart may help children having difficulty. This would keep the columns in line and help the children remember the place values. Have them cross out numbers and rename on the chart. The bottom row is the answer space.

hundreds	tens	ones
	3	0
	1	2

3-4 OBJECTIVE: **Check subtraction using addition.**

The **difference** (answer) added to the number subtracted (**subtrahend**) must equal the original number (**minuend**): 5 - 4 = 1 Check: 1 + 4 = 5

MULTIPLICATION

Use the terms multiplier, multiplicand, and product.

$$
\begin{array}{r}
5 \\
\times 4 \\
\hline
20
\end{array}
\longrightarrow
\begin{array}{l}
\textbf{multiplicand} \\
\textbf{multiplier} \\
\textbf{product}
\end{array}
$$

Review   Multiplication facts, illustrating problems with manipulatives, and writing problems that have been illustrated. *(Refer to pages 57-58.)*

Tip   While multiplication is more easily understood by combining equal groups, it should also be taught as it relates to combinations. *I have 3 shirts and 2 pairs of shorts, how many different outfits will I have?*

3-4 OBJECTIVE: **Relate multiplication and division as inverse operations.**

Multiplication combines equal groups. Division separates one group into several equal groups. The product (total in the combined group) in multiplication can be divided by one factor and result in the other factor. For example, 3 x 5 = 15. If I take 15 objects and divide them into 3 piles, there will be 5 in each pile.

3-4 OBJECTIVE: **Review and use the commutative property.**

Two factors can be multiplied <u>in any order</u>: 3 x 4 = 4 x 3 Help students visualize this by illustrating the problem, then turning the illustration and writing the new number expression *(page 59)*. To understand this property, students must realize that no objects have been added or taken away, only the position has changed. Understanding this saves time when memorizing basic facts. For example, if they know 3 x 4 is 12, they don't need to count by fours to find 4 x 3, they just recite "12."

3-4 OBJECTIVE: **Find multiples of a number.**

Counting by a number is the greatest aid to increasing speed in multiplying until children have memorized the multiplication facts. It is also used to list multiples.

Multiples   The products when multiplying a number by a factor.
                         Multiples of 4: 1 x 4 = **4**   2 x 4 = **8**   3 x 4 = **12**   4 x 4 = **16**

Practice   Relate repeated addition and multiplication.
                         4 + 4 + 4 = ?   3 x 4 = ? (3 fours)

To solve the addition, encourage the child to count by that number as far as he can before counting on to finish the addition. Arranging the addition in rows that increase by one addend provides a pattern and helps reinforce counting by that number.

    4 + 4 + 4 + 4 =   4 x 4 =
    4 + 4 + 4 + 4 + 4 =   5 x 4 =
    4 + 4 + 4 + 4 + 4 + 4 =   6 x 4 =

3-4 OBJECTIVE: **Memorize basic facts 0 - 9 times 0 - 9.**

Once the facts are memorized, learning to multiply by ten, and then by other two-digit numbers and greater, is much easier. However, many children struggle with the facts. Spend time with activities suggested for teaching the commutative property and finding multiples, use manipulatives to practice the facts, and be certain the student realizes what multiplication is and why memorizing the facts is worthwhile. (Shorthand addition—it's fast.)

Move on to other topics, but set aside time each day to drill. Work on twos through fives regularly. Let them count by the number using their fingers to mark each progression when trying to recite the answer to a flash card or oral problem. (4 x 5: 4, 8, 12, 16, 20 lands on finger five.) This also helps keep their place if they are counting on from one multiple to find the next.

Practice multiplying 2-digit numbers by 2-5, and teach procedure. Continue working on memorization of 6-9 during that short time set aside for drill. Have the student make a multiplication chart as a reference when working with problems involving facts that haven't been retained. Multiplying by ten and eleven are easily learned because they each have a simple pattern and should be introduced, along with twelves, whenever you think the student is able.

Introducing zero as a factor

Begin with repeated addition: $0 + 0 + 0 = 0$ Ask: how can this be written as multiplication? 3 x 0. Have them practice with various combinations until they recognize the pattern: any number multiplied by zero is zero (*zero property of multiplication*).

Multiplying by one

The *identity property of multiplication* tells us that a number multiplied by one is that number. While students are relating multiplication to addition, include multiplication by one, directing them toward the recognition of this property.

3-4 Objective: **Multiply one-digit numbers by ten.**

Begin with manipulatives. 3 x 10: Set out 3 columns with 10 in each column. Notice each column makes a bundle of ten. It's the same as 10 x 3. Children should be able to count quickly by tens to arrive at thirty. Give them a few practice problems with manipulatives and record the equations in a column so that students see the pattern.

$$2 \times 10 = 20$$
$$3 \times 10 = 30$$
$$4 \times 10 = 40$$

Ask them to guess <u>5</u> x 10 (i.e., <u>any digit</u> x 10) by trying to find the pattern. They should recognize that the answer to ten times any number simply requires adding a zero to the number.

3-4 OBJECTIVE: **Multiply one-digit numbers by multiples of 10.**

Background   Memorization of basic facts and ability to mentally multiply by ten (above). If facts aren't memorized, have students refer to a chart in order to focus on finding the pattern.

Teach   Practice multiplying by multiples of ten by writing a problem two ways, allowing students to see a pattern. Then give them written problems to multiply mentally.

3 x 3 tens	= _9_ tens	6 x 7 tens	= _42_ tens	8 x 4 tens	= _32_ tens
3x 30	= _90_	6 x 70	= _420_	8 x 40	= _320_

3-4 OBJECTIVE: **Multiply one-digit numbers by multiples of 100, 1,000.**

Extend the lessons above, helping students find the pattern: multiply the basic fact, add zeros.

8 x 3 hundreds	= 24 hundreds	5 x 3 thousands	= 15 thousands
8 x 300	= 2400	5 x 3000	= 15,000

Another approach:

8 x 300	= 8 x 3 x 10 x 10	basic fact: 8 x 3	times	2 tens—add 2 zeros
5 x 3000	= 5 x 3 x 10 x 10 x 10	basic fact: 5 x 3	times	3 tens—add 3 zeros

3-4 OBJECTIVE: **Multiply a 1- to 4-digit number by a 1- to 4-digit number.**

Teach in the following order:

Multiply:
1. basic facts (above).
2. 1-digit by a multiple of 10.
3. 1-digit by multiples of 100 and 1,000.
4. 1-digit by 2-digit, no renaming.
5. 1-digit by a 3-digit number, no renaming.
6. 1-digit by 2- and 3-digit, renaming.
7. 2- and 3-digit by multiples of 10.
8. 2- and 3-digits by 2-digits.

After mastering #8 students should be able to multiply any 2 numbers.

Multiplying according to a procedure *(algorithm).*

Background   Multiplication with basic facts, understanding of grouping by tens and renaming.

1. Illustrate problems with place value bars when introducing the procedure. Remind students that they could find the answer by adding, but you will show them how to multiply.

    There are 4 science classes with 21 students in each class. How many students in all? 21 + 21 + 21 + 21, or 21 x 4. They can set out the bars, 4 sets of 2 tens and 1 one. That is, 20 four times, and 1 four times. 21 x 4 is 20 x 4 plus 1 x 4

 Whether a problem is written 21 x 4 or 4 x 21: they could make 4 groups (lesser number) of 21 (greater number) to make it easier to solve (commutative property). Or, use graph paper. Students can draw a border around a rectangle 21 squares by 4 squares or the reverse (however the problem is written). That rectangle can be divided with a line separating 20 x 4 and 1 x 4.

36 x 7: 7 sets of 3 tens and 7 ones.   Or a graph paper rectangle 36 squares by 7 squares
       30 x 7 plus 6 x 7   Divide the rectangle into 30 x7 and 6 x 7

23 x 4 (23 across, 4 down)   Divide into 20 x 4 and 3 x 4

			20	x 4															3	x	4

2. Begin with simple factors of facts already memorized: 2, 3, 4 and 5 are usually first. Increase the number being multiplied from 2 to 3 digits before multiplying by higher numbers.

3. Teach the procedure with numbers that won't involve regrouping, then teach regrouping within this same range before practicing with greater numbers. A chart may help some children keep numbers aligned. Use place value manipulatives as needed.

Procedure without renaming: one-digit multiplier
Multiply the multiplier times the number in the ones place. Write the product below the ones column. Multiply the multiplier times the number in the tens place. Write the product below the tens column, to the left of the number you wrote below the ones column.

Procedure with renaming
Multiply the multiplier times the number in the ones place. If the product is ten or more, write the number of tens above the other number in the tens place. Write the number of ones left below the ones column in the answer space. Now, multiply the multiplier times the original number in the tens place, then <u>add</u> the number you wrote above it. Write the total below the tens column, to the left of the number you wrote in the ones column.

tens	ones
1	
2	6
x	3
7	8

26 x 3   Trade 10 ones for 1 ten.   <u>Solving with aids</u>   <u>The Procedure</u>

```
        tens ones          1
         2   6            2 6
        x    3           x 3
         7   8            7 8
```

4. Continue with this procedure for hundreds, extending the chart to the hundreds place.

  Students need to recognize the pattern that renaming ten in the ones place means adding a one to the place to its immediate left. They can then multiply numbers with three digits and more.

Procedure for multiplying by a 2-digit number

Since students can already multiply by a one-digit number and by multiples of ten, show them that they can already multiply two-digit numbers:

$54 \times 26 = 54 \times 6 + 54 \times 20$

```
        54
    x   26
       324   this is 54 x 6
      1080   this is 54 x 20
      1404   they have been added together
```

Next, teach the algorithm.

Step 1   Multiply the digit in the ones place of the multiplier times the multiplicand.

2	**first**
54	6 x 4 is 24.
x 26	Write the 4 and
324	carry over the 2 tens.

then
6 x 5 is 30 plus the 2
Write 32

Step 2   Write a zero in the ones place below the first product. Multiply the digit in the tens place of the multiplier times the multiplicand.

```
       54       First I write a 0, because my multiplier is in the tens place.
     x 26       Next I multiply 2 x 4 and write down 8. There's nothing to carry.
      324       Now I multiply 2 x 5 and write down 10.
     1080       There's no more to multiply, so I add my two answers.
     1404
```

Step 3   Add the two numbers to get the product.

Practice with 2-digit numbers times 1-, 2-, and 3-digit numbers before moving on. Then students should be able to extend this procedure to any number of places.

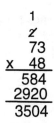

$$
\begin{array}{r}
1 \\
\not{2} \\
73 \\
\times\ 48 \\
\hline
584 \\
2920 \\
\hline
3504
\end{array}
$$

 If students seem confused by having more than one number carried above the same place, have them cross out the number as soon as it is used.

3-4 Objective: **Multiply a 2-digit number by multiples of 10, 100, 1,000.**

Background Multiplication of 1-digit numbers by multiples of 10, 100, 1,000, and practice multiplying 2-digit numbers.

Have students apply the same technique used in multiplying a one-digit number by 10, 100, and 1,000.

21 x 20	21 x 2 tens	= 42 tens	= 420	or 21 x 2 x 10
43 x 50	43 x 5 tens	= 215 tens	= 2150	or 43 x 5 x 10
13 x 3000	13 x 3 thousands	= 39 thousands	= 39000	or 13 x 3 x 10 x 10 x 10

3-4 Objective: **Multiply money less than ten dollars by a 2-digit number.**
(Grade 4)

Students should follow the procedure for multiplying whole numbers, but add the decimal point and dollar sign to the answer (product). With money, there are always two places after the decimal point. The dollar sign is always placed in front of the dollars. If students find this difficult, have them spend more time with basic multiplication and place a decimal point and dollar sign in their answers, explaining that now the answer indicates money.

3-4 Objective: **Estimate products by rounding.**

Students must first have practice rounding, and then multiplying by 10, 100, and 1,000.

3-4 Objective: **Determine common multiples.**
(Grade 4)

First, list 10 multiples of 2 numbers. Have students find numbers in common.

6: 6, 12, **18**, 24, 30, **36**, 42, 48, **54**, 60   *Some* common multiples of 6 and 9:
9: 9, **18**, 27, **36**, 45, **54**, 63, 72, 81, 90   18, 36, 54

When they are able (and this may not be until next year) have students list the multiples of each number being compared. If they can't count by the number, let them use a calculator to find the multiples and circle those multiples in common. Because there would be an endless list of multiples, give students a limit of 10 to 15 multiples for the lowest number in the comparison. Let the highest multiple in this set determine the highest possible multiple used for the other numbers in the comparison. Exclude zero as a factor since any number times zero is zero.

Find any common multiples for the numbers 2, 3, and 5 in a range determined by the first 15 multiples of 2.

> 2:   2, 4, 6, 8, 10, 12, 14, 16, 18, 20, 22, 24, 26, 28, 30
> 3:   3, 6, 9, 12, 15, 18, 21, 24, 27, 30
> 5:   5, 10, 15, 20, 25, 30

The student begins with the <u>greatest</u> number being compared (5). As he looks at each multiple, he checks the other lists looking for a match in all three: 5 – no match; 10 – one match in the 2 list; 15 – one match in the 3 list; 20 – one match in the 2 list; 25 – no match; 30 - yes, in all lists. Thirty is the only common multiple.

Pattern

If you set the limit, or include within the limit, *the product of the numbers being compared,* the student should eventually notice that it *will always produce a common multiple.* If only one common multiple is needed, that is the quickest way to find one. (2x3x5 = 30)

DIVISION

Use the terms: dividend, divided by, divisor, equals, quotient.
The number in the group to be divided is the **dividend.** The **divisor** indicates how many groups to end up with. The **quotient** indicates how many will be in each of the new groups.
$$2\overline{)6} \quad \text{or} \quad 6 \div 2 = 3 \qquad \textbf{dividend: } 6 \qquad \textbf{divisor: } 2 \qquad \textbf{quotient: } 3$$

"I have 6 items to divide into two equal groups. Now I have 3 in each of the two groups."

Make one card with a division symbol ÷ and one with a division box large enough for number cards. *Provide practice with both division symbols.* Students should recognize that $a \div b = c$ is the same as $b\overline{)a}$.

3-4 OBJECTIVE: **Identify the relationship of division to multiplication.**

1. Begin with multiplication facts: factors up to 9 x 9 and their products.

If students know the multiplication facts, they know the corresponding division facts. Give them practice with the related numbers and manipulatives to reinforce this understanding:

Arrange 12 objects to illustrate the following: 4 x 3 = 12, 3 x 4 = 12, 12 ÷ 4 = 3, 12 ÷ 3 = 4

4 x 3 = 12 (4 in each of 3 rows)

12 ÷ 4 = 3 (12 objects divided into groups

or $\frac{3}{4\overline{)12}}$ of 4 each—total 3 rows of 4.)

3 x 4 = 12

12 ÷ 3 = 4

(12 objects divided into groups of 3, a total of 4 rows of 3.)

Types of problems for practice 6 x ? = 30   24 ÷ 6 = ?   18 ÷ ? = 6

2. Have students experiment to determine whether division can use the associative and commutative properties that are part of multiplication. *(no)*

Associative   (8 ÷ 4) ÷ 2   would be equal to   8 ÷ (4 ÷ 2)
Solve what is in parentheses first: 2 ÷ 2 = 1   8 ÷ 2 = 4
They are not equal.

Commutative   8 ÷ 4   would be equal to   4 ÷ 8
8 ÷ 4 = 2   4 ÷ 8 = $\frac{1}{2}$
They are not equal.

3. Introduce division of numbers with remainders using an approach called *successive subtraction. (Understanding this will help in solving word problems.)*

19 ÷ 4 How many fours?

```
  19
- 4   (1)
  15
- 4   (2)
  11
- 4   (3)
   7
- 4   (4)
   3   Remainder
```

Here we see 4 fours and a remainder of 3.

These problems can also be done on a number line.

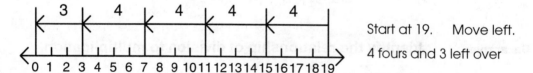

Start at 19.   Move left.

4 fours and 3 left over

4. Provide word problems requiring division.

There are 12 pies to distribute evenly to 6 families. How many pies will each family get?

Students could use 12 objects, distributing one to each of 6 groups until the 12 are all distributed. Then they would count the number in each group. Now have the students write the problem. Do more of this same type (just change numbers and objects) until the relationship of actions with the objects and the division symbols seems well understood.

5. Provide word problems that involve successive subtraction.

Barbara has 154 stamps in her collection. Each page of her stamp album holds 32 stamps. How many pages are filled? How many stamps are left? *(4 pages, 26 stamps left)*

3-4 OBJECTIVE: **Divide 1- to 4-digit dividends with a 1- or 2-digit divisor without and with remainders.**

Teach the procedure (algorithm)

Division problems using a procedure (the division algorithm) will be solved more easily if the student knows basic addition, subtraction, multiplication and division facts. Sometimes the delays in using these facts in solving a division problem cause a student to forget his place (what to do next). He should also have had practice in estimating, since a great deal of effort can be saved by guessing the correct number the first time when deciding how many times the divisor "goes into" the part of the dividend being divided. It is also necessary in order to decide whether or not the final answer is reasonable.

1. Introduce the procedure using a place value chart and manipulatives to help students follow the reasoning. Begin with evenly divided dividends.

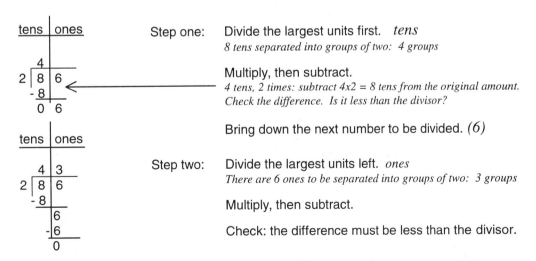

2. Once students are able to follow the sequence: *divide, multiply, subtract, check, bring down*, and repeat. Teach them how to divide numbers that have a difference after subtracting.

Again, use the place value chart. Illustrate with manipulatives if necessary. You will notice on the chart that the entire amount is brought down. This is to help the students understand the concept before memorizing the procedure.

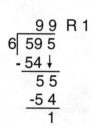

hundreds	tens	ones
2	4	3
4 9	7	2
-8		
1	7	2
-1	6	
	1	2
	-1	2
		0

1. Divide the largest unit. *hundreds*
    2 hundreds, 4 times: 2x4 = 8. Subtract from original amount.
    172 left to be divided. Trade the 1 hundred left for tens: 17 tens.

2. Divide the next largest unit. *tens*
    17 tens divided into 4 groups is 4. Multiply 4x4 = 16. Subtract 16.
    12 left to be divided. Trade the 1 ten for ones: 12 ones.

3. Divide the next largest unit. *ones*
    12 ones into 4 groups: 3   3x4 = 12 to subtract.

Progress to reasoning without the place value chart or manipulatives. Remember, the greatest remainder possible is always one less than the divisor. Arrows may help keep numbers aligned, or students may work on graph paper.

6) 5 9 5

1. This says divide 595 into 6 equal groups. Start with the largest units first.

$$\frac{9}{6)\,59\,5}$$

2. There are only 5 hundreds, not enough for six equal groups, so we trade them for tens. 59 divided into six equal groups: How many in each group? (6 x 9 is 54, less than 59. 6 x 10 is 60, more than 59, so I write 9.)

$$\frac{9}{6)\,59\,5}$$
$$-54 \downarrow$$
$$5$$

3. I multiply 9 x 6 = 54 and subtract 54 from 59. I have 5 tens left to combine with the five ones remaining.

$$\frac{99\ R\ 1}{6)\,59\,5}$$
$$-54 \downarrow$$
$$55$$
$$-54$$
$$1$$

4. 5 tens and 5 ones is 55 ones. I know 9 x 6 = 54, almost enough. I write 9. I multiply 9 x 6 = 54 and subtract it from 55. One is left. One is not enough to make a group of 6, so it is a remainder.

Sometimes students forget to write zero in the quotient. Be sure they realize that every time they proceed to the next smaller unit something must be recorded. Remainders are listed after a capital R.

$\frac{2}{13)271}$		$\frac{2}{13)271}$		$\frac{20\ R\ 11}{13)271}$	
-26	Divide	-26 ↓		-26	If necessary, continue
1	Multiply	1 1	Bring down	1 1	the sequence. Multiply
	Subtract		Divide: must write		0x13 =0. Subtract 11-0.
	Check Is the difference		something. Not enough?		Check: 11 is less than
	less than the divisor?		Write zero.		There are no more units to
					divide: 11 is the remainder.

Check division by multiplying.

Students should be taught to check the quotient using multiplication: quotient times divisor = dividend. This should not be difficult to understand if they have related multiplication facts to division facts. When they have a remainder, however, they may become confused. The remainder should be added to the product. The final total should equal the quotient.

$$76 \div 3 = 25 \text{ R } 1 \quad \text{Check: } 3 \times 25 = 75, \text{ plus } 1 = 76.$$

Practice

Practice computation problems in the following sequence of difficulty:

❑ One-digit divisors with 1- and 2-digit quotients, with and without remainders.
❑ One-digit divisors with 3-digit quotients with and without remainders.
❑ Two-digit divisors with 2-, then 3-digit quotients, with and without remainders.

3-4 OBJECTIVE: **Divide by 10, 100, 1,000 without and with a remainder.**

1. Use place value manipulatives to demonstrate.

2. Provide problems in order, allowing students to recognize a pattern.
   Ask: How are the quotients the same? (same first digit) different? (number of zeros)
   Ask: How are the quotients and the number being divided the same? (number of zeros)

$6 \div 3 = 2$	$12 \div 4 = 3$
$60 \div 3 = 20$	$120 \div 4 = 30$
$600 \div 3 = 200$	$1200 \div 4 = 300$

TOPIC: **FRACTIONS**

Teach using the following sequence:

1. Recognize fractions.
2. Compare and order like fractions.
3. Add and subtract like fractions.
4. Recognize equivalent fractions and mixed numbers.
5. Compare and order unlike fractions.
6. Write fractions in lowest terms.
7. Add and subtract unlike fractions and mixed numbers.
8. Convert fractions to decimals.

3-4 OBJECTIVE: **Match a written fraction to a shaded region.**
                       Match a written fraction to a fractional portion of a group.

3-4 OBJECTIVE: **Identify and explain the meaning of numerator and**
                       denominator.

Continue activities described in *Teaching K-2, pages 74-76. Be sure children recognize that parts must be equal for a fraction to be represented. Students should work with models before pictures, and tell the name of a fraction before writing it.*

	Region	**Group**
Numerator	parts shaded	number of items in the subset
Denominator	total number of equal parts	number of items in the set

 It may help children having difficulty with the group concept to use an empty egg carton for the set so that they can easily count how many could be held (denominator). Place an object in each of several compartments for the numerator. Cut cartons into various size sets to vary the denominator.

Practice

1. Have students name and write fractions for a variety of regions (use shapes divided into equal pieces) and groups.

2. Relate fractions to proportions.
   Put objects that vary in just 1 attribute (size, shape, or color) in a bag. Have students pull out a given number then write the fraction (or select the correct fraction card) that answers which part is (bigger, circles, yellow). *A bag of red circles and triangles: "Pull out 8. How many of the 8 are circles? Find (write) the fraction that shows that." If 5 are circles, the answer would be 5/8.*

3. Use real-life word problems that can be acted out if necessary.
   Twelve children are to share 4 candy bars equally. How much will each child get? Eight pies are to be shared equally by 24 families. How much pie will each family receive?

4. Have students cook following a recipe that includes fractions.
   Let them figure out how to double or triple the recipe. When they chop a fruit or vegetable, have them stop when they think they've chopped the amount the recipe calls for. Check their estimate with a cup measure.

3-4 OBJECTIVE: **Compare and order like and unlike fractions.**

Begin with like fractions (same denominator). Students can refer to fraction bars or pie pieces to compare fractions. They should recognize a pattern: when the denominator is the same, the greater numerator represents more.

Like Fractions

Compare $\frac{3}{4}$ and $\frac{2}{4}$ Use fraction bars or count pie pieces.

Write $\frac{3}{4} > \frac{2}{4}$

Order $\frac{1}{4}, \frac{3}{4}, \frac{2}{4}$ Compare pairs and arrange least to greatest.

$\frac{1}{4}, \frac{2}{4}, \frac{3}{4}$

Unlike Fractions

Compare $\frac{1}{6}$ and $\frac{2}{4}$ Line up appropriate fraction bars.

Write $\frac{1}{6} < \frac{2}{4}$

Order $\frac{3}{8}, \frac{1}{6}, \frac{2}{4}$ Compare pairs with fraction bars.

$\frac{1}{6}, \frac{3}{8}, \frac{2}{4}$

Equivalent Fractions   Fractions that represent equal amounts.
$1/2 = 2/4 = 3/6$ and so on

3-4 OBJECTIVE: **Write equivalent fractions.**

Teach the concept.

1. Give each student a strip of paper. Have them fold it in half, then open it and color one half. Fold it again, then in half again. This time when they open it the strip is divided into fourths. By looking at the colored section, they see 2/4 is the same amount (equivalent) as 1/2. Follow this procedure again to discover eighths. Use a new strip and begin with thirds. Color 1/3, and fold into sixths and twelfths.

2. Develop a sense of fraction sizes when denominators differ: Ask students to guess when comparing two fractions, then line up fraction bars to check.

Is 3/4 a little more, a little less, or about the same as 2/3?

3. Have children experiment with fraction bars to find equivalent fractions and record their findings. Make a chart.

Fraction	Is the same as:
$\frac{1}{2}$	
$\frac{2}{3}$	
$\frac{6}{8}$	

4. Give students a model of a fraction of a group and have them write the fraction represented with two equivalent fractions.

(model)   ▨ ▨ ▨ ☐ ☐ ☐   (student writes:) $\frac{3}{6}$, $\frac{1}{2}$

5. Provide written equivalent fractions and have students make the illustration.

3-4 OBJECTIVE: **Identify fractions as mixed numbers.**

Use models to teach mixed numbers as a combination of whole numbers and fractions. Show the whole divided into the same number of parts as the fraction, shading the entire shape. Have students name and write mixed numbers for models and make models for mixed numbers.

$$1 \quad + \quad 1 \quad + \quad \tfrac{1}{4}$$

$= 2\tfrac{1}{4}$

3-4 OBJECTIVE: **Write fractions in lowest terms.**

Background   Knowledge of equivalent fractions.

Lowest Terms   A fraction is in lowest terms when the numerator and denominator have no factors in common. (4/8 reduced to 1/2, not to 2/4: students should recognize equivalent fractions.)

Procedure   Students look at a fraction and ask themselves, what is the greatest number that can be divided evenly into <u>both</u> the numerator and denominator?

The greatest number that can be divided evenly into both is the *greatest common factor.* List factors of each number. Which is the <u>greatest</u> factor on both lists. Divide the numerator and denominator by this number.

Reduce 6/8:   Factors of 6: 1, **2**, 3, 6   GCF *(greatest common factor)*: **2** $6 \div 2 = 3$
                Factors of 8: 1, **2**, 4, 8 $8 \div 2 = 4$

The fraction in lowest terms is 3/4.

Shortcut   List factors of the smaller number and find the largest of those that can
                    be used to divide the other number evenly.

A fraction can be reduced with continual division, although this is not efficient. A
student may recognize that the numerator and denominator are even numbers and begin
with two. That answer may also be even, and they might divide by two again. They must
continue dividing by common factors until the only common factor left is *one*.   Reduce
8/16: both can be divided by 8 to get 1/2. If they don't see the 8, they should realize both
are even and can get results by beginning with 2 as a divisor: 8/16 to 4/8 to 2/4 to 1/2.

   When you divide and multiply by the same number you get an equivalent
        fraction because of the relationship between multiplication and division.
        Multiply the numerator and denominator of 1/2 by 2 to get 2/4. Divide the
        numerator and denominator of 2/4 by 2 and get 1/2.

3-4 OBJECTIVE: **Add and subtract fractions, and fractions and mixed
                        numbers.**

To add and subtract, fractions must have the same denominators.

1. Fractions with the same denominators: Have students illustrate the problem with
    fraction bars or pies to learn why only the numerators (parts shaded) are added.

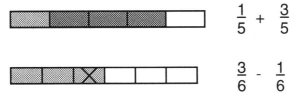

2. Fractions and mixed numbers with the same denominators: Continue with
    illustrations.

3. Unlike fractions are taught after practice comparing, ordering, and finding equivalent
    fractions. By now students should realize that denominators must be the same;
    therefore, unlike fractions must be changed to like fractions before they can be added
    and subtracted.

4. With mixed numbers: Students should first practice writing a mixed number as a
    fraction and vice versa. They should also be able to write the number one as any
    fraction (same numerator and denominator: 3/3) When adding or subtracting, begin

with the fraction, then the whole number. In subtracting it may be necessary to "borrow" (regroup/rename). Reduce the whole number by one and write one as a fraction. 2 – 1/4 would be 1 4/4 – 1/4.

When borrowing (renaming), add numerators. 2 3/4 = 1 + 4/4 +3/4   Rename: 1 7/4

Check for like denominators.	Find equivalent fractions with like denominators.	Rename if needed.	Subtract fractions.	Subtract whole numbers
$5\ \frac{1}{4}$ → $-3\ \frac{2}{3}$ *not alike*	$5\ \frac{3}{12}$ → $-3\ \frac{8}{12}$	$4\ \frac{15}{12}$ → $-3\ \frac{8}{12}$	$4\ \frac{15}{12}$ → $-3\ \frac{8}{12}$ $\frac{7}{12}$	$4\ \frac{15}{12}$ $-3\ \frac{8}{12}$ $1\ \frac{7}{12}$

$$\frac{1}{4} = \frac{1\times3}{4\times3} = \frac{3}{12}$$

$$\frac{2}{3} = \frac{2\times4}{3\times4} = \frac{8}{12}$$

$$5\ \frac{3}{12} = 4 + \frac{12}{12} + \frac{3}{12}$$

3-4 OBJECTIVE: **Convert fractions and mixed numbers to decimals.**

Background   Practice recognizing, comparing, and ordering fractions: tenths and hundredths. *(Refer to pages 74-76 , and 111-113 as needed.)*

Convert only denominators of 10 and 100.

Conversion of tenths	3/10	= 0.3
Conversion of hundredths	3/100	= 0.03

Students must recognize decimal place values. They write the numerator of the fraction in the proper decimal place. 23/100 = 0.23 The numerator uses two places, but is read 23 hundredths because the last digit is in the hundredths place. Children sometimes find this confusing and may need to review reading decimals.

TOPIC: # ROMAN NUMERALS

Here is a contrast to our place value system. It is especially enjoyable when studied as part of a history unit on ancient Rome. Point out examples of the modern use of Roman numerals on some clocks and watches. The year a movie is released is also written in Roman numerals in the end credits of most movies. If students find this topic too confusing, teach Roman numerals at a later grade.

3-4 OBJECTIVE: **Identify the value of Roman numerals I V X L.**

Memorize the value of the symbols   I = one   V = five   X = ten   L = 50

3-4 OBJECTIVE: **Write the value of Roman numeral combinations in our number system.**

Read the numeral left to right, adding the value of the symbols. When a symbol of less value is in front of a symbol of greater value, subtract it and add that total to the previous total.

     XIX would be 10 + (10 - 1) = 19   LVIII would be 50 + 5 + 1 + 1 + 1 = 58

When the symbol 1 or X is in front of a symbol of greater value, subtract.
IX means one less than 10.   XL means 10 less than 50.

I = 1	II = 2	III = 3	IV = 4	V = 5	VI = 6
VII = 7	VIII = 8	IX = 9	X = 10	XI̲X̲ = 10 + 9̲ = 19	

3-4 OBJECTIVE: **Write numbers fifty and less with Roman numerals.**

Place symbols in order—greatest value to least to be added. Use a one in front V and X for a four and a nine. Place an X in front of an L for 40.

TOPIC: # DECIMALS
Teach tenths (compare, order, add, and subtract tenths) before teaching hundredths.

3-4 OBJECTIVE: **Using a block of 100 squares, identify shaded tenths, and hundredths.**

3-4 OBJECTIVE: **Relate decimals to fractions: tenths, hundredths.**

3-4 OBJECTIVE: **Identify place value to tenths, then hundredths.**

Teach decimals during a unit on fractions.

Graph paper cut into 10 x 10 centimeter squares can be used for models of hundredths. One square unit represents 1/100, one strip of ten represents 1/10, and the entire square represents one whole. Shade rows or columns and have students tell, and write, the fraction (number of tenths first). Use shaded whole squares to represent whole numbers. Combine these with tenths to represent mixed numbers.

1. Have students identify a variety of illustrations (2 1/10, 5/10, 8/10, etc.)

2. Use a place value chart with ones, a decimal point, and tenths.

ones	.	tenths
	.	

Explain that everything to the right of the decimal point is less than one. The first place represents ten<u>ths</u> (3/10 can also be written 0.3). Place the illustrations on the chart (whole squares under ones, shaded tenths in the tenths place. Introduce hundredths later.) Let them practice writing the decimal illustrated.

3. Have students practice writing fractions and mixed numbers as decimals.

$$3 \frac{3}{4} = 3.75$$

4. Have students compare and order decimals in tenths before moving on to hundredths:

   $0.6 > 0.3$ $2.1 < 3.4$ $0.3, 0.6, 2.1, 3.4$

Follow the above procedure for hundredths.

3/100 is three hundredths   0.03 is read three hundredths.   It uses 2 places after the decimal point.

$2 \frac{7}{100}$ is written 2.07 $\frac{43}{100} = 0.43$ $3 \frac{56}{100} = 3.56$

If students are confused that both the tenth and hundredths place are used to show hundredths, illustrate with money. $0.44 can be 4 dimes and 4 pennies, or 44 pennies (44 out of 100 pennies. 100 pennies makes one dollar, $1.00).

3-4 OBJECTIVE: **Compare two decimals with place value through tenths, then hundredths.**

3-4 OBJECTIVE: **Order decimals least to greatest.**

Compare and Order decimals

First compare decimals by looking at an illustration (shaded tenths). Then students should compare digits, left to right, as they did with whole numbers. They must be aware of place value. Writing the numbers on a chart with columns keeps them aligned.

2.6 and 1.3   1 is less than 2, so 2.6 > 1.3.
12.34 and 12.36   The 4 and 6 are the first different digits. 4 is less than 6, so 12.34 < 12.36.

Order decimals (arrange least to greatest) by comparing two at a time.

3-4 OBJECTIVE: **Add and subtract decimals with same and different place value.**

1. Have students use place value manipulatives to solve the problems so that understanding precedes memorization of a procedure.

2. Begin with problems that have the same place value. Have students rename as they did with whole numbers. The place to the left of a digit is always ten times more. Ten tenths make one whole. If they must borrow a whole, they trade for ten tenths.

3. Introduce problems with different place values, still using manipulatives. 4 + 0.3 can now be determined by counting.

The Procedure (without manipulatives)

Line up the decimal points, if place values differ, write equivalent decimals (write zeros), add or subtract normally, then write the decimal point in the answer.

```
      4.8        55.7       4.0        4 - .25 would be written  4.00
    + 3.6      -18.9      + 2.5                                 -0.25
      8.4        36.8       6.5
```

Note: 4, 4.0, and 4.00 are equivalent.
            .25 and 0.25 are equivalent

As a transition from manipulatives to simply following a procedure, have students write the problem on a place value chart or graph paper with appropriate headings. (Answers are written in the bottom row on the sample chart below.)

	tens	ones	.	tenths	hundredths
Write in problem:→			.		
			.		
Write in answer: →			.		

3-4 OBJECTIVE: **Round decimals to the nearest whole number.**

3-4 OBJECTIVE: **Estimate sums, differences, by rounding.**

Tenths   *Consider five tenths or more as one and add it to the one's place.*

Round   3.6   .6 count as one.   3 + 1 = 4   3.6 rounded is 4.0
Round   12.5   .5 count as one   12 + 1 = 13   12.5 rounded is 13.0

Consider less than five tenths as zero (not enough to be considered almost one)

Round   3.4   .3 count as zero   3 + 0 = 3   3.4 rounded is 3.0
Round   12.1   .1 count as zero   12 + 0 = 12   12.1 rounded is 12.0

Hundredths   *Consider fifty hundredths or more as one and add it to the one's place.*

Round   3.65   .65 count as one   3 + 1 = 4   3.65 rounded is 4.0

Round   12.58   .58 count as one   12 + 1 = 13   12.58 rounded is 13.0

Consider less than fifty hundredths as zero.

Round   3.41   .41 count as zero 3 + 0 = 4   3.41 rounded is 3.0
Round   12.19   .19 count as zero 12 + 0 = 12   12.19 rounded is 12.0

Students should notice that less than half (tenths or hundredths) means replacing the digits with zeros but not changing the whole number. More than half replaces the digits with zeros but increases the whole number by one. When they can do this mentally, they can estimate sums and differences. 12.43 + 18.62 would be 12 + 19 = 31. 6.4 - 3.5 would be 6 - 4 = 2.

TOPIC: **MONEY**

3-4 OBJECTIVE: **Recognize and count money up to $20.00.**

To help children recognize the value of a nickel, dime, quarter, half-dollar, and dollar, ask them to find as many combinations of coins as they can to represent the value of each.

Nickel	Dime	Quarter	Half-dollar
1 nickel	1 dime	1 quarter	a half-dollar
5 pennies	2 nickels	2 dimes, 1 nickel	2 quarters
	10 pennies	5 nickels	5 dimes
	1 nickel, 5 pennies	25 pennies	10 nickels
		1 dime, 3 nickels	50 pennies
		*	*

various combinations of pennies and other coins

3-4 OBJECTIVE: **Make change up to $20.00.**

This can be combined with subtraction. If making change is the only goal, allow the student to use a calculator to figure out the amount due, then use money to illustrate that amount.

Practice

1. Make a chart listing items and the cost of each. Give the children money and ask them to purchase as many items as possible with what you have given them. If they are able, also ask how much change they will get back. For example, give a child $2.00 in a combination of coins and/or bills. Ask, "What can you buy for $2.00? What change will you get?" Problems can be solved using paper and pencil or by acting it out. Some children may need to purchase one item at a time, getting the change before deciding what to buy next.

2. Make up word problems for students to solve. *I have $1.00. I buy a notebook for 49 cents. What will I receive in change?*

Two of a variety of ways to reason: 49 cents is almost 50. 100 take away 50 is 50. Now I must add the penny between 49 and 50. My change is 51 cents. OR I know 49 and 49 is 98, which is 2 cents from one dollar. I add 2 cents to 49 and get 51 cents.

3-4 Objective: **Add and subtract dollars.**

Background   Read dollars and cents using symbols.
                        $2.25 *two dollars and twenty-five cents*
                        Add and subtract whole numbers through hundreds.

Procedure   Line up numbers in a column with the decimal points in a straight line. Calculate the answer. Place a decimal point in line with the others (or count right to left and place it after two digits). Put the dollar sign in front of the number of dollars.

It is important that numbers and decimals are lined up carefully, and the decimal point placed properly in the answer. It may help some children to use a chart with a column for dollars and cents (tens and ones in each) and a decimal point already printed in each row (the decimal points should be vertically aligned).

dollars	.	cents
	.	
	.	

Practice

1. While playing store, purchases are added. Word problems can use the sales chart: Sales for each day for 4 days were? (list 4 totals) How much was collected for the four days? Students list the amounts in a column, add, and place the decimal point and dollar sign in the answer.

2. Subtraction word problems would involve the change due, and combine the objectives of subtracting and making change if related to playing store. The student writes the amount paid, subtracts the price, puts the decimal point and dollar sign in place in the answer, then counts out that amount of change.

3. Provide several numerical (not word) problems for practice with procedure and as practice in addition and subtraction.

☞ If students have difficulty relating addition and subtraction of money to ordinary addition and subtraction, use dollar bills, dimes and pennies as manipulatives and show them how to work with the pennies (ones), then dimes (tens), then dollars (hundreds).

| **3-4 OBJECTIVE:** | **Multiply and divide money less than $10.00 by a one-digit number.** |

| **Background** | Multiply and divide by 1-digit numbers (1-9). |

Multiplication and division are carried out normally. The only difference is the decimal point.

In division, it is placed in the quotient directly above its place in the dividend (after the whole number). In multiplication, have students look at the product, count 2 places right to left, and place the decimal point.

Divide.	Add decimal point.	Multiply.	Add decimal point and dollar sign.

$$4\overline{)\begin{array}{c}42\\ \$1.68\\ \underline{1\ 6}\\ 8\\ \underline{8}\\ 0\end{array}}$$

$$4\overline{)\begin{array}{c}.42\\ \$1.68\end{array}}$$

$$\begin{array}{r}\$1.25\\ \times\ 4\\ \hline 5\ 00\end{array}$$

$$\begin{array}{r}\$1.25\\ \times\ 4\\ \hline \$5.00\end{array}$$

| **TOPIC:** | # TIME |

| **3-4 OBJECTIVE:** | **Tell whether a time is before or after another time.** |

| **3-4 OBJECTIVE:** | **Recognize time zones.** |

| **3-4 OBJECTIVE:** | **Recognize units of time, including B.C. and A.D.** |

A.M. = hours from midnight to noon (also written a.m.)
P.M. = hours from noon to midnight (also written p.m.)
60 seconds = 1 minute
60 minutes = 1 hour
24 hours   = 1 day
7 days   = 1 week
28-31 days = 1 month
12 months = 1 year
10 years   = 1 decade
100 years = 1 century
B.C. (before Christ) – the years preceding Christ's birth *(written after the date: 63 B.C.)*
A.D. (anno Domini—*"in the year of the Lord"*) — from Christ's birth on *(written before the date: A.D. 325)*

| **3-4 OBJECTIVE:** | **Tell time to the minute.** |

Use a clock with a face and 2 hands.

Telling time <u>after</u> the hour. Students start at the 12 and go forward toward the one.

To 5 minutes Have students count by fives starting at the 12 (the "zero mark" when counting forward) and moving to the right toward the number pointed to by the long hand. When they are secure with 6 representing 30 (30 seconds of a minute, and/or 30 minutes of an hour) they can start counting at thirty and continue by fives. (The same for the quarter hour marks: starting at 15 or 45.)

Students should be able to say the time when looking at this clock or when reading the time written in symbols. A colon is placed between the hour and minutes. 4:00 is read 4 o'clock

4:10 would be read "Ten minutes after four" as well as "four ten." Be sure children understand the meaning of digital read outs by having them tell the time using "minutes after" or making the same time on a clock with hands.

To the minute Have students count by fives to the number closest to the long hand, then count forward or back the number of single lines to that hand. 4:11 would be "5 - 10, 11. 11 minutes after 4"

4:38 would be "30-35,36,37,38" OR "30-35-40, back: 39,38: 38 minutes after 4"

Telling time <u>before</u> the hour Students start at the 12 and move backward, toward 11.

By five minutes Count by fives moving to the left from the 12. Read the time as __ minutes before (hour). (E.g., 20 minutes before 3 o'clock.)

By one minute Count by fives moving to the left from the 12 to the nearest number before the long hand, then count on by ones. Read the time as ___minutes before (hour). (E.g., 22 minutes before 3 o'clock.)

Have students practice reading the same time on a clock as both minutes before and minutes after. 4: 35 35 minutes after 4 25 minutes before 5

When figuring time from a digital clock, subtract the minutes from 60 to find the minutes before the next hour. 4:35 60 - 35 = 25 The next hour after 4 is 5
25 before 5 is the answer.

3-4 OBJECTIVE: **Find elapsed time.**

3-4 OBJECTIVE: **Solve word problems using time: schedule, clock, calendar.**

Begin with relevant situations and informal procedures before using subtraction.

1. Provide a written **schedule** and ask children at what times certain events occur and how much time is spent on certain events (reading a schedule):
   - What time does John do his homework?
   - How long does he spend on homework?
   - Who spends more time on homework, John or Bob? (Provide two schedules to be compared.)

Clock

2. Begin with times up to 5 minute intervals (not to the minute) for easier calculations.

   Give children two times and ask them to find out how long it is from one time to the other. Begin with real-life situations. For example, *"Bedtime is 9:00. It is now 8:10. How long until you have to be in bed?"*

3. Let children count to find the time before teaching them to write it as a subtraction problem. *(Refer to page 190.)* They would begin with the earlier time and count by 5 or 10 minute intervals to the next time—8:10 to 8:20 is 10, 8:20 - 8:30 (10 more) 8:30 - 8:40 (10 more) 8:40 - 8:50 (10 more) 8:50 - 9:00 (10 more): 5 tens, which is 50 minutes.

   They can keep track of each ten on a finger then count the fingers. Be certain they do not count the first number (a frequent error), but realize they are counting the *passing* of 10 minutes. (Notice in the example above that 8:10 <u>to</u> 8:20 is the first ten, they would not hold up a finger when they say "8:10," the starting point. Rather, they would wait until they said "8:20.") It may help to move the clock hand as they count. When it reaches the 4 they would count the first ten.

   When the time is to the minute, count the tens, then add ones as you count forward from there: From 8:10 to 8:53 count <u>10 to 20</u> (first ten), <u>20 to 30</u> (another ten), <u>30 to 40</u> (ten more), <u>40 to 50</u> (ten more) is 4 tens and from 50 to 53 (count by ones) is 3. So, 4 tens plus 3 is 43 minutes.

Calendar

4. Have students practice reading a date: month and number. *(Today is April twelfth.)*

5. Students should find
   - Days before and after other days *("Which day is two days before Tuesday?")*
   - How many days until ___. *("Today is Thursday, the field trip is next Monday.")*
   - How many days in (#) weeks *(Be sure they can point out one week on the calendar.)*
   - The day a certain date falls on. *("John's birthday is the tenth. What day is that?")*
   - The date a certain day falls on. *("The third Friday of the month.")*

TOPIC: **GEOMETRY**

3-4 OBJECTIVE: **Identify line segment, ray, intersecting, parallel and perpendicular lines.**

At this age a **line segment** refers to a straight line, or a straight line connecting two points. *(While it is actually a straight curve, the shortest path between two points, this becomes confusing as we tend to think of all curves as arc-shaped. Therefore, refer to straight and curved lines according to common usage, as do the examples and explanations in this guide.)*

A **ray** is a line with only one endpoint. That is, it extends without end in one direction. We indicate this by showing the endpoint and drawing the line like an arrow: •——⟶

Intersecting lines have a common point. (They meet or cross.) **X**

Perpendicular lines intersect at a point that forms right angles. **L T +**

Parallel lines *never* have a common point (never intersect). **II**

A **plane** is a flat surface that goes out in all directions. Lines are drawn in a plane. **Shapes** are drawn with lines, and are, therefore, *plane figures. At this age the term shape continues to be used more frequently than plane figure, however the teacher should be aware of the mathematical explanation.*

Have children look for parallel, perpendicular, and intersecting lines in objects—windows, chairs, bookshelves—and make examples of these lines with objects (straws, pencils, string). Note that all lines defined above are (visually) straight lines. Don't accept examples with curved lines.

3-4 OBJECTIVE: **Identify shapes (plane figures) as open or closed.**

Closed figures have an inside and an outside, open figures do not.

3-4 OBJECTIVE: **Identify the following shapes:**
Have students make examples of each on a geoboard.

Polygon   A figure made by joining at least three line segments. (*Poly* means "many," *gon* means "sides.") Shapes with curved areas would not be polygons. Have students decide if a drawing is a polygon or not.

yes   no   yes   no
        (one side not a segment)   (segments not all joined)

After they identify figures as polygons or not, ask if all polygons are closed figures. *(Yes, all sides are joined.)* Are polygons plane or solid figures? *(Plane—they are flat.)* Here you may point out that you have been referring to plane figures as shapes (i.e., in the K-2 lessons), and will continue to use that term. Students merely need to be aware that both are correct.

Quadrilateral   A polygon with four sides. Have students find or make polygons with four sides.   *(A geoboard is handy for these exercises.)*

Parallelogram   Make a rectangle with straws and tilt it to the right to demonstrate a parallelogram. Include parallelograms in activities with other shapes.

Right triangle   A triangle with one right angle.
(Angles are discussed on the following page.)

Isosceles triangle   A triangle with two sides that are equal in length.

Equilateral triangle   A triangle with all three sides equal in length.

3-4 OBJECTIVE: **Given a shape (plane figure): find a line of symmetry, the number of angles, the faces, edges and vertices.**

Continue activities with shapes as described in *Teaching K-2,* pages 70-74. As students are able, use suggestions in *Teaching 5-6*, pages 191-195.

3-4 OBJECTIVE: **Identify a right angle and other angles as greater than or less than.**

Angles are formed by two rays with the same endpoint. The endpoint is called the vertex.

Perpendicular lines form right angles. Compare angles made with rays with a right angle. Is the angle greater than or less than the model? Compare angles in polygons.

right angle   **greater than**   **less than**

3-4 OBJECTIVE: **Identify a slide, flip, and turn of a plane figure.**

Have students make a shape on the geoboard so that they can turn the board to view the shape in various positions. Use cutouts to flip.

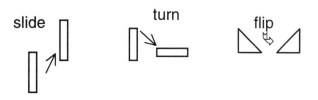

3-4 OBJECTIVE: **Identify figures as congruent, similar.**

Congruent   Figures that are the same size and shape.

Similar   Figures that are the same shape but not necessarily the same size.

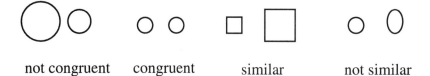

not congruent   congruent   similar   not similar

Logic books are available for practice with visual discrimination and include a variety of lines, figures, letters, and pictures that are flipped or turned.

3-4 OBJECTIVE: **Identify parts of a circle: center point, diameter, radius.**

circle   A simple closed curve* with all points the same distance from the center.

diameter   A line from one side of the circle to another <u>that passes through the center point</u>.

radius   A line drawn from the center point of the circle to the edge.

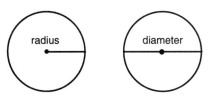

Simple closed curves may be discussed briefly since the term is used here. However, to prevent confusion, use the term curve according to common usage and only provide examples of figures with visual curves. (Mathematically, shapes such as triangles and squares are simple closed curves because, by definition, a curve connects two points and a simple curve is a curve that does not pass through any point more than once. Such an explanation is unnecessary at this level.) A <u>closed curve</u> returns to its starting point so that there are no end points. You must cross (intersect) a point of a <u>simple</u> closed curve if you try to draw a line from the inside to the outside. The circle is special because all lines drawn from the center of the circle to points on the circle are the same length.

Practice

Provide circles and center points. Have students draw and measure diameter or radius.

Children have heard and used the term "circle" for a variety of purposes—"circle the correct answer" or "sit in a circle." Now they should become aware of the exactness necessary for a figure to actually be defined as a circle.

3-4 OBJECTIVE: **Measure the perimeter and the area of polygons.**

Perimeter   The distance around a polygon.

Students should measure each side, then add the numbers to find the total. If connecting cubes are available, ten together as a "chunk" can be used to *estimate* perimeter.

Area   The amount of surface within the lines of a polygon.
    Area is measured in **square units.**

Practice

Explore perimeter and shape (geometry)

1. Can more than one shape have the same perimeter?

    Give the student a large rubber band and a geoboard. How many shapes can he make with that one rubber band? Or place a length of string tied at one end on a table and have him shape each vertex with his fingers.

2. How does changing the size of an angle (increase or decrease) change the shape?

Explore area

3. Draw outlines of polygons on graph paper (or use tiles or a geoboard).
    Students should count squares and record (or tell) the area of each.

4. Give one area (number of square units). Have students make several shapes all with the same area.

6 square units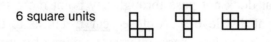

5. Estimate by chunking. Have a child line up boxes on the floor along one edge. Using those as a unit, he estimates how many rows he will need to fill the room. As he is able, have him do these types of activities mentally. *"I think 8 boxes will fit along that edge. Then I can do that about 4 more times. 4x8 is 32."* For volume, he would continue: *"Then 5 layers would reach the ceiling. That's 32 x 5 boxes."* Here he can multiply mentally by multiplying 5 x 3 tens (150) plus 5 x 2. 150 plus 10 is 160 boxes.

3-4 Objective: **Identify solids (space figures): cube, sphere, cylinder, rectangular prism, cone, and pyramid.**

Teach the correct terms rather than continuing with box (cube), ball (sphere) and can (cylinder). Continue with activities in *Teaching K-2*, pages 72-74. Students should identify the number of faces (flat surfaces), edges (where two faces meet) and corners (where edges meet) of each. Move on to *Teaching 5-6*, pages 191-194 as students are able.

3-4 Objective: **Measure volume.**

Background Determine area in square units.

Review A flat figure has an area. It has two dimensions—length and width. Measurements are in square units (how many squares fit in the space: square inches, square centimeters, square feet). Solids, or space figures, have three dimensions—length, width, and height. A square unit doesn't have height. Volume refers to the space inside the figure. It's measured with cubes. *("How many cubic units fit inside?")*

Teach Have students build rectangular prisms with cubes. One layer is one cube in height. Students should record the volume of their models by counting cubes.

Analysis

1. Does each layer have the same number of cubes? *(Yes.)*
2. How could you find the number in one layer without counting every cube? *(Multiply the number in a row times the number in a column: length times width.)*
3. How could you find the total in 2 layers without counting? *(Add the number in the first layer twice or multiply the number in the first layer by two.)*

Instead of counting each cube, then, you can use the formula Volume = length x width x height. (V = lwh)

1. Give students a volume and have them build models (rectangular prisms).

2. Provide measurements for all three dimensions and have students find volume. (Be sure answers are in cubic units.)

TOPIC: **MEASUREMENT**

Procedure: choose a unit, compare it to the object, record the number of units.

3-4 OBJECTIVE: **Recognize symbols, abbreviations for units, and the value of metric prefixes.**

Length
12 inches (in)	= 1 foot (ft)
3 feet	= 1 yard (yd)
1760 yards	= 1 mile (mi)
5280 feet	= 1 mile

Metric
100 centimeter (cm)	= 1 meter (m)
1,000 meters	= 1 kilometer (km)

Weight
16 ounces	= 1 pound (lb)
2,000 pounds	= 1 ton

Metric
1,000 grams	= 1 kilogram

Metric Prefixes
centi	one hundredth
milli	one thousandth
deci	tenth
kilo	thousand

Capacity
16 ounces (oz)	= 1 pint (pt)
2 pints	= 1 quart (qt)
4 quarts	= 1 gallon (gal)

Students should read and write the appropriate symbols after the number when solving problems of measurement.

3-4 OBJECTIVE: **Convert units of measure within a system from smaller to larger.**

Give students measurements to convert for practice.
5 quarts = *1 gallon 1 quart*   29 inches = *2 feet 5 inches*   9 feet = *3 yards*

3-4 OBJECTIVE: **Choose the appropriate unit for measuring an item.**

1. Review as needed and continue with activities listed in *Teaching K-2* on pages 62-68 to develop a sense of length, capacity, and weight. Use a variety of informal and formal units when estimating and checking. For example, have children look at a distance and guess how far it is in feet, then walk it. Was the guess to little? too much? Practice with more distances in feet to increase awareness of feet as a unit.

2. Have students practice measuring with formal units and the appropriate tools (ruler, weights, cup measure). Teach fractions of an inch gradually: measure to "about a" whole, then half, then quarter.

3. Have students choose the appropriate unit of measure for various situations, giving them a choice. For any child that has not grasped which types of units are used for specific types of activities, begin with choices farfetched choices—"Gallons or inches?" Remember, however, that the goal is to lead him to a sense of quantity within a "family": pints, quarts, or gallons.

4. Teach conversions to help increase understanding of quantity within a "family."

   "1,000 grams is a kilogram. A feather weighs about a gram. Would you weigh yourself in grams or kilograms?"

5. Estimate temperatures and read thermometers in both Celsius and Fahrenheit, matching a temperature with a situation. It helps to have certain temperatures connected to basic information that can be used as a framework for guessing: room temperature (20°C, 68°F), freezing (0°C, 32°F) and boiling point (100°C, 212°F) of water.

3-4 OBJECTIVE: **Estimate an answer using the appropriate measure in a situation where no hint is given.**

Provide opportunities for students to estimate without suggesting a unit. When they check, using the unit they suggest, it will refine their ability to choose appropriately.

3-4 OBJECTIVE: **Add and subtract measures.**

Use simple measures within the same unit that can be counted to find the answer. Have able students convert answers within a system for addition problems.

2 quarts + 3 quarts = *5 quarts* (or *1 gallon 1 quart*)

Problems can use abbreviations for units as students are able.

6 in + 7 in = *1 ft 1 in* *(The student converts 13 inches to feet and inches.)*

12 oz + 9 oz = *1 lb 5 oz* *(The student converts 21 ounces to pounds and ounces.)*

25 cm - 8 cm = *13 cm*

19 qt - 13 qt = *6 qt*

208 ft - 34 ft = *174 ft*

GRADES 5 - 6 OBJECTIVES

Emphasize
Mastery of algorithms
Use of formulas

Provide Opportunity
To use calculators
To program computers

Involve Students In
Reasoning
Problem Solving

Items introduced at this level are in italics.

PROBLEM SOLVING

❑   **Solve a variety of types of problems.**

- **Reasoning**:
  - Classify.
  - Compare.
  - Find patterns.

- **Computation:**
  - Add.
  - Subtract.
  - Multiply.
  - *Divide.*

- **Collect, Record, Analyze Information:**
  - Pictograph.
  - Bar graph.
  - Line graph.
  - Circle graph.
  - Maps.

- **Word Problems:**
  - Choose the operation.
  - Solve one-, two-, *three- and four*-step problems.
  - Solve problems requiring more than one type of operation.

❑   **Understand how to solve problems requiring up to 4 steps.**

1. Understand what the problem is asking.
   What does it require: an exact answer, estimation, collecting information?
2. Decide which information to use.

3. Make and carry out an appropriate plan.
4. Check the answer.

❏ **Use problem solving strategies.**

- **Solve problems mentally.**
  - Count on or back to find sums and differences.
  - Compare numbers.
  - Use a pattern.
  - *Draw conclusions.*
  - *Check for correct form.*
  - Use associative, commutative, and *distributive* properties.

- **Estimate.**
  - Front-end estimation.
  - Chunking (unitizing).
  - Using rounded or approximate numbers.

- **Use pencil and paper.**
  - Draw a picture to define the problem.
  - Write a number sentence.
  - Use a formula.
  - Carry out an operation (add, subtract, multiply, *divide*).
  - Determine the mean, median, mode.

- **Use a calculator.**
  - Compute whole numbers, decimals, fractions, *intergers, and percent.*

- **Use a computer.**
  - Use software.
  - Learn programming skills.

PROBABILITY AND STATISTICS

❏ **Determine range, mean (average), median, mode.**

❏ *Explain a fraction as probability.*

❏ **Determine probability of an event occurring and not occurring.**

❏ *Determine the probability of outcomes as equally likely or not.*

❏ *Use diagrams to illustrate predicted outcomes.*

RATIO, PROPORTION, PERCENT

❑ **Ratio**

- *Understand and identify ratios.*
- *Identify equal ratios.*

❑ **Proportion**

- *Understand the concept of proportion.*
- *Solve problems of proportion.*

❑ **Percent**

- *Understand the concept.*
- *Convert decimals to percent and vice versa.*
- *Convert fractions to percent and vice versa.*
- *Find the percent of a number.*
- *Estimate.*
- *Find interest.*

WHOLE NUMBER CONCEPTS AND COMPUTATION

❑ **Understand concepts.**

- *Recognize a variety of ways to express a number.*
- *Write a number expression with symbols when given only words.*
- *Give the meaning of a number expression written with symbols.*
- *Solve number expressions using the order of operations.*
- *Identify prime and composite numbers.*
- Write number sentences for word problems.

❑ **Understand place value.**

- Identify place value *through billions (grade 5) and trillions (grade 6).*
- Given a number *through billions* in words, write it in standard form.
- *Identify the place value of any digit in a number written in standard form.*
- Convert numbers from standard to expanded form and vice versa.
- Compare and order numbers.
- Round up to the *nearest million.*
- *Write the standard form for a number written in exponential form.*

ADDITION

- Add sums *through the millions.*
- Add mentally: 2 numbers of 1-, *2-, 3-, and 4-digits.*
- Add mentally: 2, *3, and 4* numbers of 1- and 2-digits.
- Estimate sums using rounding and front-end estimation.
- Retain: Addition facts; Adding up to 6-digit numbers.

SUBTRACTION

- Subtract numbers with differences *to one million.*
- Subtract mentally *1-,2-, and 3-digit numbers from 3- and 4-digit numbers.*
- Estimate differences using rounding and front-end estimation.
- Retain: Subtraction facts. Subtract numbers up to six digits each.

MULTIPLICATION

- *Identify factors, prime factors, common factors, greatest common factor.*
- *Multiply with exponents.*
- Identify multiples, *least common multiple.*
- Use commutative, identity, and zero properties of multiplication.
- Multiply mentally 3 and 4 numbers which are multiples of 10.
- Multiply mentally 3 and 4 one- and two-digit numbers.
- Estimate products using rounding.
- Multiply 1-, 2-, *3-, 4-, and 5-*digit numbers by multiples of 10.
- Multiply 1-, 2-, 3-, *4-, and 5-*digit numbers by 1-, 2-, *3-,and 4-*digit factors.

DIVISION

- Recognize a fraction as division (1/2 is one divided by two).
- *Determine divisibility by 2, 3, 5, 9, 10.*
- Divide 1-digit divisor, quotients < 10, without and with remainder.
- Divide 1-digit divisor, 2- and 3-digit quotients, without and with remainder.
- Divide 2-digit divisor, quotients < 10, without and with remainder.
- Divide 2-digit divisor, 2- and 3-digit quotients, without and with remainder.
- Divide 3-digit divisor, 4-, 5-, and 6-digit dividends.
- Estimate quotients.

FRACTIONS

❏ **Understand concepts.**

- Identify a fraction as a shaded region and as a part of a group.
- Write an improper fraction as a mixed number and vice versa.
- Write equivalent fractions.
- Write a fraction in lowest terms (simplest form).
- Compare, order: proper, improper fractions, mixed numbers with like, and unlike denominators.
- Plot fractions on a number line.
- Write a fraction as a decimal (including repeating decimals).

❏ **Solve computation problems.**

- Add and subtract fractions and mixed numbers with like and unlike denominators.
- Multiply a fraction times a whole number.
- Multiply fractions and mixed numbers.
- Divide fractions and mixed numbers.
- Solve word problems involving fractions.

ROMAN NUMERALS

❏ **Identify the value of symbols I, V, X, L, *C, D, M*.**

❏ **Write the standard number for combinations of Roman numerals (IV = 4) and vice versa.**

NUMBER BASE SYSTEMS OTHER THAN BASE TEN

❏ **Write a number in standard form in another base and vice versa.**

DECIMALS

❏ **Understand concepts.**

- Recognize and write decimals *to the hundred-thousandths.*
- Using an illustration, write decimals as fractions, *percents, and with words.*
- Compare and order decimals *to hundred-thousandths place.*
- *Round to the nearest tenth, hundredth,* and whole number.
- Estimate sums, differences, *products, and quotients.*

❏ **Solve computation problems.**

- *Add and subtract through hundred-thousandths place: same and different place value.*
- *Multiply a decimal by a whole number, a power of ten, a decimal.*
- *Mentally multiply a decimal by a power of ten.*
- *Divide a decimal by a whole number.*
- *Divide a decimal by a power of ten.*
- *Divide a decimal by a decimal.*
- *Round quotients.*

POSITIVE AND NEGATIVE INTEGERS

❏ *Understand, identify and write integers.*

❏ *Compare and order integers.*

❏ *Add and subtract integers using properties of integers.*

ALGEBRA

❏ *Evaluate algebraic expressions when given a value for the variable.*
25 - c when c = 9

❏ *Graph ordered pairs on a grid. (Use positive and negative integers.)*

MONEY

❏ Add, subtract, multiply, divide by a whole number.

❏ Handle money: count, make change.

❏ *Choose the better buy: unit pricing.*

❏ *Estimate prices: round to the nearest dollar.*

TIME

❏ Calculate elapsed time.

❏ Use schedules in problem solving.

GEOMETRY

- ❑ **Identify lines:**

    - Line segment, ray.
    - Intersecting lines.
    - Parallel lines.
    - Perpendicular lines.

- ❑ **Identify *and classify* shapes according to their properties.**

    - Identify circle, square, rectangle, polygon, quadrilateral, trapezoid, parallelogram, and right, isosceles, and equilateral triangles.
    - Identify parts of a circle: center point, diameter, radius.

- ❑ **Identify and classify solids according to their properties.**

    - Identify the number of angles, faces, edges, and vertices.

- ❑ **Identify slides and flips of a figure.**

- ❑ **Identify figures as congruent, similar, symmetrical.**

    - Find a line of symmetry.

- ❑ **Identify, *draw and measure* angles.**

    - *Construct and bisect angles.*

- ❑ **Solve problems.**

    - Measure perimeter of polygons.
    - *Measure area of polygons using a formula.*
    - Determine the volume of a rectangular prism in cubic units using a formula.
    - *Find the surface area of a rectangular prism using a formula.*
    - *Find the volume of a cylinder using a formula.*
    - *Measure the circumference of a circle using a formula.*
    - *Find the area of a circle using a formula.*
    - Solve problems involving perimeter, area, and volume.

MEASUREMENT

❑   **Read *and use* symbols and abbreviations for units, and the value of metric prefixes.**

❑   **Convert from smaller to larger measurements within a system** (feet to miles, cups to quarts).

❑   **Choose the appropriate unit for measuring when told what is to be measured.**

❑   **Estimate an answer using the appropriate measure in a situation where no hint is given**. *(How much water will this bucket hold?)*

❑   **Use measurements from scale drawings in problem solving.**

❑   ***Determine the more precise measurement.***

❑   **Estimate, measure and solve problems of length, capacity (liquid volume), temperature, and weight.**

- **Length**
    - to fractional part of an inch.
    - inch, foot yard, mile.
    - *millimeter*, centimeter, meter, kilometer.

- **Capacity (liquid volume)**
    - fluid ounce, cup, pint, quart, gallon.
    - milliliter, liter.

- **Weight**
    - ounce, pound, ton.
    - *milligram,* gram, kilograms.
    - Read a scale.

- **Temperature**
    - Associate temperature *with events.*
    - Read a thermometer: Celsius, Fahrenheit.
    - *Convert temperature: Celsius, Fahrenheit.*

TOPIC: **PROBLEM SOLVING**

5-6 OBJECTIVE: **Provide a variety of types of problems.**
Continue with suggestions in Teaching Grades 3-4, pages 84-88.

❑   **Reasoning**
Continue with materials that encourage inductive and deductive reasoning. Include:

1. Practice completing tables by recognizing a pattern.

2. Practice recognizing a pattern using information in a complete table and using it to make a prediction. (This is often part of analyzing information listed below.)

☞   Students should realize that two numbers are not enough to predict a pattern. Sometimes three is enough, but generally more numbers are needed for the pattern to be obvious.

❑   **Collect, Record, Analyze Information**
Continue with use of pictographs, bar graphs, and tables. Add practice interpreting line and circle graphs before having them draw such graphs. Include reading maps and solving problems that include scale miles.

Bar Graph   Amounts are recorded as bars and can be compared. *(See page 85.)*

Include practice with double bar graphs—two different colored bars at each interval.

Line Graph   Information showing trends over time is recorded with a dot, then dots are connected with lines. *(See page 139.)*

Both bar and line graphs begin with a *vertical* and *horizontal axis* (the perpendicular lines with the scales and labels). A line graph has a *slope. That is, the line moves up, or down, indicating an increase or decrease. (A completely horizontal line would indicate no increase or decrease.)*

Hours spent on homework

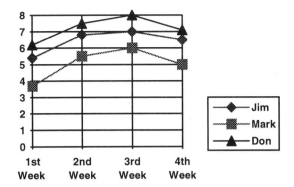

Analyzing the Data

(The example has 3 lines, many graphs have only one.)

1. Ask questions that require simply reading the information.

    - *How many hours did Jim spend on homework the first week?*
    - *How many hours did Mark spend on homework the first week?*
    - *The line for Mark from week one to week two slopes up. Does that show an increase in time spent, or a decrease?*

2. Ask questions requiring students to compare information.

    - *How many more hours did Mark study the third week compared to the first week?*
    - *Who studied the most (the fewest) hours the first week? in four weeks?*
    - *How many more (fewer) hours did Don study than Jim? than Mark?*
    - *In which week were the most total hours spent on homework?*

3. Ask questions that require thinking about a possible trend, and/or making a prediction.

    - *Was there any time that Jim, Mark, and Don studied more than usual? (3rd week)*
    - *Do Jim's hours of study follow a pattern? What about Mark's and Don's? (They all increase to the third week, then decrease.)*
    - *Any possible explanations? (Maybe exams)*

Practice

1. Have students record information on labeled graphs.

2. Teach students to make a graph when given information, or include collecting the data. Have students determine the range of the numbers given to decide on the scale. Place numbers on the vertical axis and time intervals on the horizontal axis.

Topic Ideas

- Graph scores. (E.g., spelling test scores, bowling scores, and/or time spent exercising each day.)

- Graph sales of an item during a class fund-raising drive.

- Coordinate with science units—record observations, and draw conclusions.

- Coordinate with history/geography—use an almanac to record population, number of lakes, and so on.

- Use tables and graphs found in textbooks, the newspaper, and the almanac to trigger discussion. (Practice analyzing data.)

Circle Graph   The circle represents one whole or one hundred percent. It is divided into pie sections indicating a proportion of that whole (fraction, percent).

Eye Color of Students

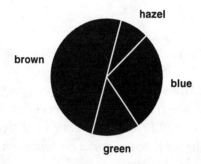

Analyzing the Data

1. Make comparisons.
   - *What is the most (or least) common eye color in the class?*

2. Interpret proportions.
   - *Does more than (or less than) (half, third, fourth) represent (color) eyes?*
   - *What fraction (or percent) have brown eyes?*

3. Interpret the amounts represented.
   - *There are a total of 20 people in the class. How many have brown eyes? (Half would be ten.)*

Word Problems   Continue to provide regular opportunities to solve word problems throughout the year. As students work within a topic, include word problems that provide application of the information they are learning. For example, during a unit on measurement, problems can involve converting ounces to pounds to find the solution.

5-6 OBJECTIVE: **Solve problems requiring up to 4 steps.**

Continue with the approach to problem solving suggested in *Teaching Grades 3-4,* pages 86-87. Encourage students to decide whether to solve a problem mentally, with a calculator, or on paper rather than automatically reaching for a pencil.

- ◆ *Can I solve it in my head?*

- ◆ *Are the numbers large or unfamiliar so that a calculator might be more accurate?*

- ◆ *Can I work faster with pencil and paper?*

- ◆ *Do I need to make a drawing or write the problem to visualize it?*

Practice

1. Provide word problems in which actions are less obvious, so that choosing whether to add, subtract, multiply, or divide takes more thought.

2. Include problems that require more than one operation to arrive at the final solution.

    Jill has a coin collection. Her album has 32 pages and each page holds 12 coins. She has 48 coins in the album. How many pages are still available?

    First the student must find out how many pages are filled: $48 \div 12 = 4$ pages.
    Then the number filled must be subtracted from the total pages in the album:
    $32 - 4 = 28$ pages

    If the final question had been "How many pages have been filled?" only the first step would be necessary; yet the problem would still have required thought. Proceed to more steps as students are able. Have them discuss their thinking with you if word problems are difficult so that you can guide their reasoning.

3. Include problems that require several steps, but not necessarily several operations.

    John found a jacket on sale for 30% off. The original price is $60.00. Sales tax is 7%. How much must Jack pay for the jacket?

    Step 1   Calculate the discount (30% of $60).
    Step 2   Subtract the discount from the original price.
    Step 3   Calculate the sales tax on the discounted price.
    Step 4   Add the sales tax to the discounted price for the total owed.

5-6 OBJECTIVE: **Use problem solving strategies.**

Continue with strategies described in the previous sections and add the following:

1. **Simplify the problem.**

    If the problem has large numbers, substitute simple, one-digit numbers in order to find a plan that works, then follow the plan with the actual figures. This is especially helpful when more than one step is required, or when the plan involves drawing a picture to help visualize the problem.

    There are 24 square tables in the restaurant, each sits one person per side. A party of 16 made a reservation and want to sit together. How many tables must be pushed together to make a rectangle large enough to seat the group of 16?

    Begin with a drawing representing 4 tables since 4x4 = 16 and children often think that's all that's required. Point out that 3 people can sit at end tables, but only 2 people can sit at middle tables.

    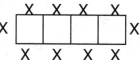

    Next, the student should count the total people at the two end tables—6, and subtract that from the total to be seated—16. 16 - 6 = 10, so tables for 10 people are still needed. They must all be middle tables, sitting two each. 2x what is 10? So, 5 middle tables are needed. (Or students may make a complete illustration and count.)

    5 middle tables + 2 end tables = 7 tables needed to seat the entire group of 16.

2. **Draw a picture, make a list of information or in some way make an illustration that helps you organize the problem** *(as in the example above).*

3. **Solve written problems mentally by using the distributive property: a x (b + c) = (a x b) + (a x c).** This property can be applied to a multiplication problem being solved mentally by breaking apart the multiplicand into an addition problem and multiplying each addend by the multiplier.

    23 x 5 = (20 x 5) + (3 x5)   115 x 3 = (100 x 3) + (15 x 3)   44 x 6 = (40 x 6) + (4x6)

4. **Estimate answers by rounding.**

    Round numbers to be used in the operation, estimating totals. This is a helpful tool in determining whether or not a calculated answer is reasonable. Students should realize whether their estimate is more or less than the actual total. (Did they round the numbers up or down?)

5. **Draw conclusions.**

    This is part of analyzing data and recognizing patterns to discover a rule. Examples are included within specific topics.

6. **Check correct form.**

Answers should be labeled correctly and in lowest terms unless instructions say otherwise.

7. **Calculator skills: include practice with integers and figuring percentages.**

8. **Computer skills: continue with practice programming.**

TOPIC: # PROBABILITY AND STATISTICS

5-6 OBJECTIVE: **Determine range, mean (average), median, mode.**

Continue to practice these skills. *(Refer to pages 88-89 as needed.)* To determine the average of several numbers, add the numbers and divide the sum by the number of addends. The quotient is the average.

5-6 OBJECTIVE: **Determine the probability of an event occurring and not occurring.**

5-6 OBJECTIVE: **Determine the probability of outcomes as equally likely or not.**

1. Continue with probability activities in general. *(Refer to pages 41-43 and 88 as needed.)*

2. Introduce outcomes that are equally likely and not equally likely.

If one outcome is just as likely to occur as another, they are equally likely. For example, tossing a coin—the chance of heads landing up is equal to the chance of tails. The spinners used in earlier grades were to be divided into equal sections so that outcomes were equally likely. Now give students a spinner on a circle with pie shapes of one half, just over one fourth, and a third wedge covering the remaining space. Ask which color would be more likely to occur? (the color of the half section) least likely to occur? (the smallest wedge). Have students practice predicting and recording probability activities, telling whether the outcomes were equally likely or not.

5-6 OBJECTIVE: **Explain a fraction as a probability.**

The number of possible outcomes is written as the denominator. The chance of one particular outcome occurring is written as the numerator.

Tossing a coin: There are 2 possible outcomes, heads or tails. The chance of heads occurring is 1/2. The chance of tails occurring is 1/2.

Rolling a number cube: There are 6 possible outcomes. (A number cube has numerals 1-6, a die with 1-6 spots could also be used.) The chance of tossing a "2" would be 1 chance out of 6 or 1/6.

5-6 OBJECTIVE: **Use diagrams to illustrate predicted outcomes.**

Use equally likely events. A **tree diagram** can be used to illustrates the possible outcomes. Each branch shows a possible outcome.

Tossing a coin: 2 possible outcomes—heads or tails. But if tossing two coins:

coin 1   heads   tails   The possibilities with one coin: heads or tails.

coin 2 heads tails   heads tails   Possible outcomes with two coins: heads + heads, heads + tails, tails + heads, tails + tails. Of 4 possible outcomes, ¼ chance for both heads or both tails; 2 out of 4 combinations of one coin being heads and one tails.

When rolling 2 number cubes each with numbers 1 - 6, the possible outcomes would look like this:

first cube: 1   2   3   4   5   6

  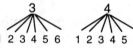

second cube: 1 2 3 4 5 6 1 2 3 4 5 6 1 2 3 4 5 6 1 2 3 4 5 6 1 2 3 4 5 6 1 2 3 4 5 6

Possible   (1,1)(1,2)(1,3) (2,1)(2,2)(2,3) (3,1)(3,2)(3,3) (4,1)(4,2)(4,3) (5,1)(5,2)(5,3) (6,1)(6,2)(6,3)
Outcomes   (1,4)(1,5)(1,6) (2,4)(2,5)(2,6) (3,4)(3,5)(3,6) (4,4)(4,5)(4,6) (5,4)(5,5)(5,6) (6,4)(6,5)(6,6)

Probability of rolling a combination of 2 and 3 [see (2,3) and (3,2) above]: 2 out of 36 possible outcomes: $\frac{2}{36}$

TOPIC: **RATIO**

5-6 OBJECTIVE: **Understand and identify ratios.**

A ratio is a comparison between two numbers.

A ratio of 6 boys out of 14 students:
Write: 6 to 14   6:14 or 6/14   Read: "There are 6 boys out of 14 students."

Practice

1. Provide students with information in various forms—verbal, written, a drawing, and a display of objects—and have them write ratios for each.

   Compare the number of triangles (4) to the number of circles (7). They write 4 to 7, 4:7, or 4/7.

Compare the number of cans of tomato soup (8) to the total number of cans of soup (10). (8 to 10, 8:10, or 8/10)

2. Have students write ratios for information on charts as part of analyzing data.

   Write a ratio for the number of students with blue eyes compared to the total number of students.

5-6 OBJECTIVE: **Identify equal ratios.**

1. Have students write equivalent fractions. Are they equal? *(Yes, that's what equivalent means.)* Write a ratio: "2 to 4" Have students write it the other two ways—2:4, 2/4 Ask for a ratio that would be equal to 2 to 4 (a fraction equivalent to 2/4: 1/2, 4/8, 6/12).

2. Give students a ratio. They must multiply each number by the same factor to find equal ratios. Using a chart helps students see the pattern. Below, the numbers in italics are those to be filled in by the student. Numbers 8 and 2 were multiplied by 2, 3, 4, and 5. These are listed outside the chart to indicate procedure only. A student would simply fill in a chart and do the multiplication mentally or on a separate piece of paper.

   Use the items in the practice problem at the top of the page, but instead of finding the ratio of tomato soup cans to the total number of cans of soup (10), find the ratio of tomato soup cans (8) to non-tomato soup cans (10 - 8 = 2). Written in fraction form, the equal ratios would be: 8/2, 16/4, 24/6, 32/8, 40/10.

soup		8x2	8x3	8x4	8x5
tomato	8	*16*	*24*	*32*	*40*
not tomato	2	*4*	*6*	*8*	*10*
		2x2	2x3	2x4	2x5

Practice

1. Have students identify ratios as equal or not to indicate understanding of the concept.

2. Have students apply the concept of equal ratios to solve word problems:

   The instructions on the instant cocoa mix suggest 4 heaping spoonfuls to 1 cup of hot water for a single serving. How many spoonfuls will be needed to serve 6?

TOPIC: **PROPORTION**

5-6 OBJECTIVE: **Understand the concept of proportion.**

Proportion represents two ratios that are equal.

6:3 and 3:1 are equal ratios called a proportion. It is read *"six is to three as three is to one."*

The ratios can also be written in fraction form.

Twenty-seven is to nine as fifteen is to five. $\frac{27}{9} = \frac{15}{5}$

5-6 OBJECTIVE: **Solve proportion problems.**

An equation indicating two ratios are equal is called a proportion. $\frac{2}{5} = \frac{n}{25}$ *is such an equation.* To find the value of *n*:

$$\frac{2}{5} = \frac{n}{25}$$ 2 x ? = n   I know 5 x **5** = 25
    5 x ? = 25   I multiply 2 x **5** to find n   (n = 10)

Or use **cross products.** Equivalent fractions have equal cross products:

$$\frac{a}{b} = \frac{c}{d}$$ a times d = b times c

$$\frac{4}{13} = \frac{n}{65}$$ 13 x n = 4 x 65   *(Arrange the equation so the "n" is on the left of the equal sign.)*
    13 x n = 260   *(Divide 13 by 13 to get 1. 1 x n = n. What is done to one to one*
    n = 260 ÷ 13 = 20   *side must be done to the other.)*

Practice

1. Give students equations and word problems to solve.

    Solve Equations   4/5 = n/50   Find n   *(n = 40)*
        4/5 = 40/n   *(n = 50)*
        27/9 = 9/n   *(n = 3)*

    Word problems Students should write an equation and solve for the missing number.

    Jackie gets paid for working six days out of each ten-day pay period. How many days pay would she receive in a month?

    To solve

    Step 1   Write the first ratio—6 days out of 10 as a fraction: 6/10

    Step 2   Write the equal ratio, a letter for the unknown number. 6/10 = n/30
        (30 days/month)

    Step 3   Think, ten times what is 30? *(3)* Use that same factor to multiply 6.
        6x3 = 18, so 6/10 = 18/30.
        The answer is 18 days pay out of a 30 day *(or month)* period.

Or set up the problem using cross products.　　$10 \times n = 6 \times 30$

$$n = 180 \div 10$$
$$n = 18$$

2. Combine objectives by solving proportion problems using scale drawings, measurements, and geometry. Have students find the unknown measurement for one side of a figure by looking at a similar figure with all measurements given.

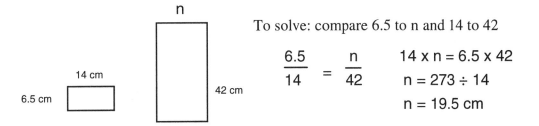

To solve: compare 6.5 to n and 14 to 42

$$\frac{6.5}{14} = \frac{n}{42}$$

$14 \times n = 6.5 \times 42$

$n = 273 \div 14$

$n = 19.5$ cm

TOPIC:　　**PERCENTS**

5-6 OBJECTIVE:　　**Understand the concept.**

Background　　Understanding of and practice with fractions and decimals.

Cent from the Latin centum means one hundred. <u>Percent</u> means per hundred. 25 percent (25%), therefore, <u>means</u> 25 <u>per hundred</u>, or <u>25 out of 100</u>. It is a ratio: 25 to 100, 25:100, 25/100. Decimals to the hundredths place can also represent percent: remember 0.25 means 25/100. Percent is written with the percent symbol % following the number: 25%.

	meaning	*fraction*	*decimal*	*ratio*
20%	"20 out of 100"	20/100	.20	20 to 100
75%	"75 out of 100"	75/100	.75	75 to 100
48%	"48 out of 100"	48/100	.48	48 to 100
2%	"2 out of 100"	2/100	.02	2 to 100

Relate percent to money. What percent of a dollar is one cent? (1%) ten cents? (10%) 25 cents? (25%) Students can visualize percent using 10x10 square centimeter graph paper or peg board, or the hundred unit from place value manipulatives. Percents greater than 100% would require full squares to represent each hundred. 234% would be illustrated with two 10x10 squares and one more that has thirty-four hundredths shaded.

Practice

Students should be aware of the common uses of percent. Have them find examples in newspapers or magazines (sales, sports scores, weather reports).

5-6 OBJECTIVE: **Convert decimals to percent and vice versa.**

Decimal to percent   Have students use place value blocks to illustrate decimals to the hundreds place. (Begin with decimals between 0.01 and 0.99, then move on to larger numbers.) How would these decimals be written to name a percent?

Write the decimal, move the decimal point two places to the right, follow the number with the percent symbol.

$$0.19 \rightarrow 19\% \qquad 0.03 \rightarrow 3\% \qquad 2.34 \rightarrow 234\% \qquad .0875 \rightarrow 8.75\%$$

Percent to decimal

Write the number without the percent symbol, then move the decimal two places to the left. $34\% \rightarrow 0.34 \qquad 5\% \rightarrow 0.05 \qquad 4\tfrac{1}{2}\% = 4.5\% = 0.045 \qquad 300\% = 3.0$

> ## Practice

1. Provide percents to be written as decimals and decimals to be written as percents.

2. Once students can carry out the procedure easily, include finding percents in word problems.

5-6 OBJECTIVE: **Convert fractions to percent and vice versa.**

Because percent means per hundred, the denominator of the fraction is always 100. 33% would be written 33/100. Provide percents for students to write as fractions using a denominator of 100, and fractions with a denominator of 100 to be converted to decimals.

Fractions in lowest terms   After writing a percent as a fraction with 100 as the denominator, have students reduce the fraction to lowest terms by dividing both the numerator and the denominator by the same divisor (greatest common factor).

Write a fraction in lowest terms as a percent.   There are two ways to change a fraction to a percent. Fractions with a denominator of 2, 4, 5, 10, 20, 25, and 50 can be changed to an equivalent fraction with a denominator of 100 because 100 can be divided evenly by each of these numbers. To change 1/5 to a decimal, the student thinks, "How many times can 5 go into 100? 20 times," then multiplies both the numerator and denominator by 20: 1/5 = 20/100. Now he writes this fraction as a percent: 20%.

After practice, students should recognize some common fractions and their equivalent percentage.

$$10\% = 1/10 \qquad 20\% = 1/5 \qquad 25\% = 1/4 \qquad 50\% = 1/2 \qquad 75\% = 3/4$$
(Provide 33 1/3% for 1/3)

$$25\% = \frac{25 \div 25}{100 \div 25} = \frac{1}{4} \qquad 40\% = \frac{40 \div 20}{100 \div 20} = \frac{2}{5} \qquad \frac{8}{10} \begin{smallmatrix} \times 10 \\ \times 10 \end{smallmatrix} = \frac{80}{100} = 80\%$$

When a fraction cannot be changed to an equivalent fraction that has a denominator of 100, divide the numerator by the denominator, extending the dividend with a decimal and zeros. Carry out the division to 3 places after the decimal. Change the decimal quotient to a percent.

Write $\frac{3}{8}$ as a percent: Divide the numerator by the denominator.

$$\begin{array}{r} .375 \\ 8\overline{)3.000} \\ \underline{2\,4} \\ 60 \\ \underline{56} \\ 40 \\ 40 \end{array}$$

Write the decimal as a percent by moving the decimal two places to the right. .375 = 37.5%

5-6 OBJECTIVE: **Find the percent of a number.**

To find the percent of a number change the percent to a decimal and multiply the number by the decimal.

Decimal: 25% of 800 → .25 x 800 = 200   15% of 32 → 0.15 x 32 = 4.80
            1% of 32 →   .01 x 32 = .32   31% of 160 → .31 x 160 = 49.60

If sales tax is 6% and the purchase is $25.00, what is the tax?
Think: 6 % of $25.00 → 0.06 x 25.00 = 1.50 = $1.50

Practice

1. Provide the percent and money amount or number. Students practice the above procedure.

2. Have students practice finding 10% of a number mentally.
    (If it's a whole number, imagine a decimal after the ones place, then mentally move the decimal one place to the left: 10% of 48 = 4.8)

To find the percent of a number, change the percent to its equivalent fraction in lowest terms and multiply the number by the fraction.

Use this method only with percents whose fraction equivalents are easily remembered.

        25% = 1/4   50% = 1/2   75% = 3/4   33 1/3 % = 1/3

    multiples of 10 = n/10 or n/5 (30% = 3/10; 60% = 3/5)

Encourage students to solve the problem mentally.

25% of 800:   ¼ x 800 or 800 ÷ 4 = 200   50% of 40:   ½ x 40 or 40 ÷ 2 = 20

Practice

1. Give students the percent and the number. Have them practice calculating percent using decimals and fractions.

2. Once students are secure with the process, have them apply their skill in a real situation. During a money unit provide discount information. Make your own problems or use ads.

   Ask   What is the discount amount? *(the percent of the original price)*
             What is the final sale price? *(original amount minus the discount)*

   $25.00 sweater, 20% off. What is the discount amount? $25 x 0.20 = $5.00 discount
   What is the final sale price? $25.00 - $5.00 = $20.00

3. Continuing to apply skills to real situations, have students calculate sales tax on purchases. This could be combined with sales and discounts for multi-step problems. Be certain students calculate step-by-step, labeling answers to avoid confusion. They should realize that the sales tax would be based on the final price to be paid, not the amount before the discount.

   Follow up on the example above: $20.00 discount price plus 8% sales tax:
   $20 x 0.08 = $1.60 tax $20 + $1.60 = $21.60 to be paid.

 Allow students to use calculators when the focus is on procedure.

5-6 OBJECTIVE: **Estimate.**

Substitute approximate numbers that allow the problem to be carried out mentally or more quickly.

28% of 48 would be about 25%, or 1/4 of 48: 48 ÷ 4 = 12, so the answer would be "<u>about</u> 12."

5-6 OBJECTIVE: **Find simple interest.**

Interest involves three things: a money amount borrowed or lent, a rate of interest, and a specified length of time. The rate is given as a percent. Convert it to a decimal in order to multiply (below).

To solve   **Interest = money amount x rate x time**

The time must be written in years. A portion of a year would be written as a decimal or a fraction.   6 months = 0.5 or 1/2   9 months = 9/12 = 3/4 or 0.75

Example   Deposit $300 at 10% interest per year.
To find the interest you earn: $300 x 0.10 x 1 (year) = $30.
To find the new balance: Add the interest to the original deposit: $300 + $30 = $330.00

Example   Borrow $450 at 18% annual rate of interest (annual = 1 year)
            Interest: $450 x 0.18 x 1 = $81.00   interest you pay each year on the borrowed
                    amount.

How much interest would you pay if it were a 2-year loan? (Note: This assumes interest is paid each year and not compounded.) $450 x 0.18 x 2 = $162.00 interest.

How much interest would you pay for a 6 month loan? $450 x 0.18 x 1/2 = $40.50 interest.

Practice

1. Provide money amount, interest rate, and length of time. Have students calculate interest to practice the procedure.

2. Include these problems in a unit about money.

3. Interest is a fee paid in exchange for using someone else's money. The total interest owed depends on the original amount borrowed, the rate of interest (this is the percent), and the length of time the money is kept (before being repaid.) When banks pay interest on savings accounts, they use the money and pay you interest. If you leave the interest in your account, it is added to your original amount, and interest is paid on their total.

TOPIC: NUMBER CONCEPTS AND COMPUTATION

1. Introduce the concept with manipulatives or illustrations. Help the students reason by asking them leading questions as often as possible.

2. Provide practice using manipulatives or illustrations and simple numbers before moving on to larger numbers or a wider range of numbers.

3. Encourage memorization of concepts, facts, formulas, and procedures (algorithms).

4. Provide practice without manipulatives or illustrations.

5. Provide review of previously learned material.

6. Build speed in computation while maintaining accuracy.

5-6 OBJECTIVE: **Recognize a variety of ways to express a number.**

Students have now had a variety of experiences with number concepts, and have an extended math vocabulary. Pull these together to provide review in a way that allows students to make connections that they can draw on when solving problems mentally. Have students express one number in several ways:

written with words	*standard form*	*expanded form*	*as a fraction*
thirty-two	32	30 + 2	32/1

as a product	*as a sum*	*as a difference*	*as a quotient*
4x8	20 + 12	40 - 8	128 ÷ 4

as an expression using the order of operations   (3 x 10) + 2

5-6 OBJECTIVE: **Write a number expression in symbols when given words.**

Use this to check understanding. Students sometimes memorize procedures from models without grasping meaning. Provide choices for a statement, or have them write what you say:

| 65 is less than 95 | choose: | 65 > 95 | <u>65 < 95</u>? |
| 6 divided by 9 | choose: | <u>6/9</u>   9/6 | 9 ÷ 6   <u>6 ÷ 9</u> |

5-6 OBJECTIVE: **Give the meaning of a number expression written with symbols.**

Normally, a teacher uses several expressions for the same concept in teaching. Check to be certain that students realize different expressions can mean the same thing. This understanding is essential for solving word problems.

6 - 3 can be stated	*six minus three*	<u>or</u>	*three less than six*
7 + 5 can be stated	*seven plus five*	<u>or</u>	*five more than seven*
4 x 8 can be stated	*four times eight*	<u>or</u>	*eight multiplied by four*

5-6 OBJECTIVE: **Solve number expressions following the order of operations.**

Grade 5: practice with the rule—"<u>Do the operations in parentheses first</u>."

Have students find solutions to expressions using three numbers, two operations, and parentheses before learning more about the order.

1 + (7 x 8) would be 1 + 56, which equals 57   (1+7) x 8 would be 8 x 8, which equals 64.

*Teach the **order of operations** (grade 6).*

Step 1   Compute the operations inside the parentheses first.
Step 2   Next, multiply and divide from left to right.
Step 3   Last, add and subtract, from left to right.

Memory device for order after parentheses: M̲y D̲ear A̲unt S̲ally (M̲ultiply, D̲ivide, A̲dd, S̲ubtract).

The answer depends on the order in which the operations are carried out:

Compare   (17 - 5) x 3   and   17 - 5 x 3

(17 - 5) x 3   Parentheses first   17 - 5 x 3   Multiply first
      ↓   ↓

   12   x 3   Then multiply.   17 - 15   Then subtract
         ↓   ↓
         36   **2**

     Division is completed before multiplication if it is further left. Likewise,
        subtraction is done before addition if it is further to the left.   25 ÷ (7-2) x 3
        Order: Solve (7-2) then work left to right. (7-2) =5; 25 ÷ 5 = 5; 5 x 3 = 15.

Practice

1. Provide practice problems using any two of the four operations, with and without parentheses.

2. Include a variable and its value after students have practiced with this concept.
   n + 2 x 3 = 21   n = 5 Have students put in parentheses if needed to make this number sentence true. *(n + 2) x 3 = 21*

3. Once students recognize negative numbers, use both positive and negative numbers in practice problems.

5-6 OBJECTIVE: **Identify prime and composite numbers.**
Both refer to whole numbers greater than one, and whole number factors.

Prime number   A number with the factors one and itself only̲.

Students can find prime numbers through 100 by making a number chart 10 rows x 10 columns. Begin with number 2 in the second space *(one is neither prime nor composite)*. The second row should begin with 11 under the empty space. Circle 2, cross out all multiples of two. Circle 3, cross out all multiplies of three. Continue to circle the next number <u>not</u> crossed out, crossing out its multiples. Numbers not crossed out are prime: 2, 3, 5, 7, 11, 13, 17, 19, 23, 29, 31, 37, 41, 43, 47, 53, 57, 59, 61, 67, 71, 73, 79, 83, 89, 97.

2	3	4	5	6	7	8	9	10	
11	12	13	14	15	16	17	18	19	20
21	22	23	24	25	26	27	28	29	30
31	32	33	34	35	36	37	38	39	40
41	42	43	44	45	46	47	48	49	50
51	52	53	54	55	56	57	58	59	60
61	62	63	64	65	66	67	68	69	70
71	72	73	74	75	76	77	78	79	80
81	82	83	84	85	86	87	88	89	90
91	92	93	94	95	96	97	98	99	100

Twin primes   Two prime numbers with a difference of two.
(19 - 17 = 2; therefore, the pair of prime numbers 17 and 19 would be called twin primes.)

Composite number   A number with more factors than one and itself.

Example   Even numbers other than 2. (They have 2 as a factor.)
Multiples of any number.
26 is a composite number. Its factors are 1, 2, 13, and 26.

A composite number can also be expressed as a product of <u>only</u> prime factors:
12 = 2 x 2 x 3 *(all factors are prime numbers.)*
26 = 2 x 13   *(all factors are prime numbers)*

To find prime factors, make a factor tree. Begin with any two factors. Notice that the prime factors will always be the same.

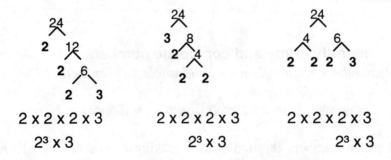

Practice

1. Give students several whole numbers. Have them list the factors and tell whether the number is an example of a composite or prime number by looking at the factors.

    25: 1, 5, 25 composite   23: 1, 23 prime   12: 1, 2, 3, 4, 6, 12 composite

2. Have students make a factor tree and find the prime factors for a variety of whole numbers.   List the factors using exponents (above illustration).

3. Find examples of twin primes using the number chart.

TOPIC:	**PLACE VALUE**
5-6 OBJECTIVE:	**Identify place value through billions, trillions.**
5-6 OBJECTIVE:	**Given a number to billions in words, write it in standard form.**
5-6 OBJECTIVE:	**Identify the place value of any digit of a number in standard form.**
5-6 OBJECTIVE:	**Convert numbers from standard to expanded form and vice versa.**

All of these objectives can be part of the same lesson at this age. Since students should have had experiences with place value charts, they should understand extending it through millions, then billions, and beyond. The bottom row in the chart below could have pockets for number cards to be used by children that prefer a hands-on approach.

TRILLIONS			BILLIONS			MILLIONS			THOUSANDS			ONES		
hundred trillions	Ten Trillions	trillions	hundred billions	ten billions	billions	hundred millions	ten millions	millions	hundred thousands	ten thousands	thousands	hundreds	tens	ones

Each section has a heading to identify the group; however, the second row names the actual place value. Begin with a review through the <u>hundred thousands</u> place with all of the above objectives before introducing more places. Have students place commas to separate digits into groups of three, counting right to left from the ones place.

Write   215,674,108,510,279

Read   *Two hundred and fifteen trillion, six hundred and seventy-four billion, one hundred and eight million, five hundred and ten thousand, two hundred and seventy-nine.*

Be certain students have realized that only digits 0 - 9 are used in our base ten system. The <u>place</u> of a digit in a number determines its value. If they have difficulty reading numbers or writing them in expanded form, go back to a place value chart and discuss the value assigned each place.

number in words	standard form	expanded form
two million fifty-six thousand fourteen	2,056,014	2,000,000 + 56,000 + 14

Naming the value of any digit
Read the number underlined and then say the place value.

2,<u>0</u>56,014	zero hundred thousands
2,056,0<u>1</u>4	one ten
<u>2</u>,056,014	two millions

Check understanding. *Ask students to write 1, 10, 100, or 1,000 more or less than a given number. Here you can see that they change the digit in the correct place.*

Practice

Activities to aid in understanding of the quantity these numbers represent:

Scale models included in astronomy materials are helpful in understanding millions and beyond. Continue with activities that will develop a sense of quantity through billions in grades 5-8 even though students are able to calculate with large numbers.

1. Give the student something to estimate. *E.g., a gallon container of dried beans. Use a cup of beans as a reference: "There are 112 beans in this cup."*

2. Discuss a reasonable range of estimates. *Within 300 would mean that any guesses of 300 more or less than 2547 (i.e, 2247 to 2847) would all be considered correct.*

3. If counting individual objects to check an estimate, have students count by grouping the objects into piles of ten and then grouping ten tens into piles of 100. (It's faster and easier to recheck this way if distracted while counting.)

How many boxes of 100 paper clips will fill a shoe box? (Estimate and check.) What is the total number of paper clips? How many shoe boxes will hold one million boxed paper clips? How many shoe boxes will fit in this room? If all those shoe boxes are filled with boxes of paper clips, how many paper clips would fit into this room? (Use a formula for volume.)

5-6 OBJECTIVE: **Compare and order numbers.**

Coordinate this with the numbers being used above. Encourage students to compare digits to determine the greater number. Some students may need to line up the two numbers, one above the other, to more easily see which digits to compare. Beginning with the greatest place value, they move to the right until they reach digits which are different. The greater digit is in the greater number.

261,<u>3</u>98   The 3 and 4 in the hundreds place are the first digits that differ.
          4 is greater than 3.

261,<u>4</u>96   That means 261,496 is greater than (>) 261,398.

If the problem was written: 261,398 ? 261,496 the student would replace the ? with a less than symbol: <

Practice

Order several numbers least to greatest by comparing two numbers at a time.

5-6 OBJECTIVE: **Round up to the nearest million.**

Since students must be able to identify the place value of each digit in a number to be rounded, only assign numbers with place values already taught. Students should recognize that if a number is to be rounded to the nearest *hundred*, the digits to the right of the hundreds place will be replaced with zeros.

1<u>6</u>5,902 rounded to the nearest *ten thousand*: 6 is in the ten thousand's place, and to its right will be zeros. Now the question is, will the six be changed? If the number to its right is 5 or more, it will increase by one (the number will be rounded <u>up</u>). If the number to the right is less than five, it will not be changed (the number will be rounded <u>down</u>). In this case, it will be 170,000. *(Refer to page 92-94 as needed.)*

Round 34,609 to the nearest thousand.

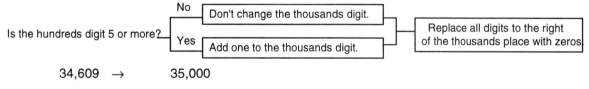

Is the hundreds digit 5 or more? — No → Don't change the thousands digit. ⟶ Replace all digits to the right of the thousands place with zeros
Yes → Add one to the thousands digit.

34,609 →   35,000

Round 34,609 to the nearest hundred.

Check the digit to the right of the hundred's place. 0 < 5. Don't change the 6. 34,600

5-6 OBJECTIVE: **Write the standard form for a number written in exponential form.**

Exponents are small numbers written above and to the right of a factor. It indicates the number of times that factor is used. It is read as "to the (<u>ordinal number</u>) power." The "second power" is often called "squared," the third power, "cubed."

$2 \times 2 \times 2$ would be written 2^3 and read "two to the third power" or "two cubed." Be certain students don't think of the exponent as a factor and try to multiply 2 by 3. They should write the 2 three times, putting in multiplication signs, and then find the product.

6^8 (6 to the eighth power) = 6 x 6 x 6 x 6 x 6 x 6 x 6 x 6 = 1,679,616

10^5 (10 to the fifth power) = 10 x 10 x 10 x 10 x 10 = 100,000

Allow students to use a calculator to find values. Have them look for a pattern and discover a rule for writing the standard form of 10 with any exponent without having to actually multiply. *(The exponent will be the same as the number of zeros.)*

 Zero is used as an exponent. The value of any factor (number being multiplied) to the zero power is one ($9^0 = 1$). Any factor to the first power is that factor ($9^1 = 9$).

TOPIC: # COMPUTATION

Students can make their own problems. Use stacks of number cards 0-9. Students draw a card from each stack to make a 2-, 3- or up to 7-digit number. Choose the math symbol, then draw cards again for the second number. A calculator can serve as the answer key.

ADDITION

5-6 OBJECTIVE: **Add numbers with sums through the millions.**

Review addition with up to 6-digit numbers, with and without renaming.

Add: 28,456 + 7,304

First: Line up the numbers. (Use graph paper, if necessary)

Add beginning with the ones place.

$$\begin{array}{r} {}^1 \quad {}^1 \\ 2\,8,4\,5\,6 \\ +\;7,3\,0\,4 \\ \hline 3\,5,7\,6\,0 \end{array}$$

Trade if necessary.   10 ones = 1 ten   15 hundreds = 1 thousand plus 5 hundreds

Once the method of adding numbers is learned, there is no limit to the place value or number of addends a student can add. Have students keep skills sharp with paper and pencil practice and drill addition facts if they have not been memorized or are not recalled quickly. Check *Teaching 3-4,* pages 96-97, for instruction if students have difficulty with addition problems.

5-6 OBJECTIVE: **Mentally add 2 numbers of up to 4 digits; up to 4 numbers of 1 and 2 digits.**

1. Look for easy combinations: add numbers that will end in zero. (3 + 7, 40 + 60)

   32 + 6 + 18 + 3 Think: 2 + 8 = 10, so 32 + 18 = 50.

   Now add the other numbers: 6 + 3 = 9.

   All together, 50 + 9 = 59   *(Addition facts should be memorized.)*

   766 +242   Think: "I know 700 and 200 is 900 and 60 plus 40 is another hundred, that's 1,000 and 6 and 2 make 8, so it's 1,008.

5-6 OBJECTIVE: **Estimate sums using rounding, front-end estimation.**

Review the front-end strategy with 3- and 4-digit numbers. Add 2 to 4 numbers. Review rounding as needed. *(Refer to pages 92-94, and 157 as needed.)*

375   Add digits with the greatest place value: 1100 (11 in the hundreds place)
724   Look at the rest of the numbers. They look like about 150 more (75 + 25 + 50)
<u>148</u>   Estimate 1250

SUBTRACTION

5-6 OBJECTIVE: **Subtract numbers with differences to one million.**

Review renaming with simple problems *(page 98).* Once the method is understood, there is no limit to the place values of the numbers students should be capable of solving. Provide pencil and paper practice to maintain skill. Drill facts if they are not memorized or are only slowly recalled.

5-6 OBJECTIVE: **Mentally subtract 1-, 2-, and 3-digit numbers from 3- and 4-digit numbers.**

Practice subtraction mentally.

5-6 OBJECTIVE: **Estimate differences using rounding and front-end estimation.**

Review and practice. *(Refer to pages 92-94, and 157 as needed.)*

MULTIPLICATION

5-6 OBJECTIVE: **Identify factors, prime factors, common factors, greatest common factor.**

Factors are the numbers being multiplied. In 2 x 3 = 6, numbers 2 and 3 are factors of 6. Every number has at least two factors: one and itself.

Prime factors are factors of a number that are all prime numbers. (See page 153.)
Prime factors of 12: 2x2x3

Common factors are found when comparing the factors of at least two numbers. Those factors in both numbers are common factors.

To find factors of 6: 1x6, 2x3, 3x2 List the factors: 1, 2, 3, 6

To find factors of 12: 1x12, 2x6, 3x4, 4x3, 6x2 List the factors: 1, 2, 3, 4, 6, 12

Common factors of 6 and 12 are factors in both lists: 1, 2, 3, 6

The greatest common factor (GCF) is the largest factor on both lists. 6

5-6 OBJECTIVE: **Multiply using exponents.**

When one number is used as a factor several times, it can be written using an **exponent**. The exponent tells how many times the number (called the <u>base</u>) is used as a factor.

In 5 x 5 x 5 x 5 the factor 5 is the base; it is multiplied 4 times. Therefore, 4 is the exponent. It is written this way: 5^4 and read "five to the fourth power."

Have students practice writing and giving the products for several bases with exponents. A common error is to multiply the base by the exponent instead of listing the number of factors and multiplying correctly. In the example, the product is 625. (5x5x5x5) NOT 20 (5x4).

Students can find the pattern for writing the product of ten to various powers without having to go through the multiplication every time. Have them list 10 to the first through fifth or sixth power, write the multiplication problem it represents and the product. Then ask them to find the relationship between the number of zeros in the product and the exponent. *(They are the same.)*

$$10^1 = 10 \qquad\qquad = \mathbf{10}$$
$$10^2 = 10 \times 10 \qquad = \mathbf{100}$$
$$10^3 = 10 \times 10 \times 10 = \mathbf{1,000}$$

1. Give students factors to write with a base and exponent.

2. Give students a base and exponent to write with factors.

3. Give students a base and exponent to write as a number in standard form. *This skill is helpful in studying other number base systems and could also be practiced during those lessons.*

5-6 OBJECTIVE: **Identify multiples, least common multiple.**

Review finding multiples and common multiples. *Counting by a number provides a list of multiples.* The least common multiple (LCM) is the smallest (least) of the multiples in common to two or more numbers. For example, 6 and 4:

6: 6, 12, 16, 24   12 is the first multiple 6 and 4 have in common. 12 is less than common multiples 16 and 24.

4: 4, 8, 12, 16, 24   The LCM (least common multiple) of numbers 6 and 4 = 12.

5-6 OBJECTIVE: **Mentally multiply 3 and 4 numbers which are multiples of ten.**

1. Multiply two numbers that are each a multiple of ten.

Understand	Procedure	
30 x 40 = (3 x 10) x (4 x 10) *expanded form*	Multiply the front digits.	3 x 4
(3 x 4) x (10 x 10) *commutative, associative properties*	Write the product.	12
	Attach the zeros.	1,200

Have students practice with several problems mentally, including several to the hundreds and thousands place. (300 x 5000—3x5 = 15, attach 5 zeros: 1500000, place commas: 1,500,000)

2. Once the procedure has been learned, multiplying 3 and 4 numbers should not be difficult. If it is, review with two numbers and explain again why it works. Provide practice problems.

20 x 400 x 30   6000 x 50 x 20 x 100   10 x 400 x 300 x 30   and so on.

5-6 OBJECTIVE: **Mentally multiply 3 and 4 numbers of 1 and 2 digits.**

Look for combinations that end in zero. (Commutative property—multiply in any order.)

　20 x 4 x 5   Think: 5 x 20 = 100, now multiply by the other number: 100 x 4 = 400

　25 x 7 x 4   Think: 4 x 25 = 100, 100 x 7 = 700.

5-6 OBJECTIVE: **Estimate products using rounding.**

Background   Rounding and multiplying two numbers that are multiples of ten.

This skill is to be used in estimating answers in word problems. (About how many?)
Practice the following techniques, then provide word problems for application.

1. Round factors to the greatest place value and multiply mentally.
    32 x 167 would be 30 x 200 = 6000

2. Round factors to the nearest ten and multiply.
    146 x 12   would be 150 x 10 = 1500

3. Round only the greater factor.
    329 x 8 would be 300 x 8 = 2400

5-6 OBJECTIVE: **Multiply 1- through 5-digit numbers by multiples of ten.**

Once students recognize the pattern of adding zeros when multiplying by powers of ten
(10, 100, 1,000) they should not have difficulty multiplying by a multiple of ten. They
multiply the numbers other than zero, and attach the appropriate number of zeros at the
end (total number of zeros in factors. They should be able to do this mentally with 1- and
2-digit numbers.

　　　3 x 90　　Think:　3x9 = 27 and attach one zero: 270
　　　9 x 700　　Think:　9 x7 and attach 2 zeros: 6300
　　　30 x 20　　Think:　3 x 2 and attach 2 zeros: 600

5-6 OBJECTIVE: **Multiply up to 5-digit numbers by 1-, 2-, 3- and 4-digit
                       factors.**

Practice a variety of multiplication problems, using the procedure taught in grades 3-4
(*page 103*). Although five-digit numbers are introduced this year, the procedure is the
same and should not cause difficulty. Watch for errors and reteach anything causing
difficulty.

Watch for possible errors.

1. Forgetting to write zeros in the partial products when multiplying by factors of 2 or more digits.

Wrong		Right	
36		36	
x 42		x 42	
72		72	(first partial product)
144		1440	(second partial product)
216		1512	

    Students may need to be shown again why this is necessary.
    36 x 42 = 36 x 40 and 36 x 2

    They are adding partial products (two in this example). The product of a number and a multiple of ten ends in zero (multiple of 100 - 2 zeros, multiple of 1,000 - 3 zeros).

2. Difficulties with the number carried over (traded):
    Forgetting to write it, forgetting to add it: drill procedure.
    Confusion over which to use when more than one has been written above a digit: students cross out the number as soon as it is added in.

Teaching Tip for Grades 5-8
Once basic facts are well known, the multiplication algorithm (procedure) is easily carried out, and students are able to mentally multiply by multiples and powers of 10, it is not necessary to assign quantities of practice pages with 3- and 4-digit multiplication problems. Include a few in mixed practice pages to keep skills polished and allow the use of calculators to find products in word problems or formulas.

TOPIC: **DIVISION**

5-6 OBJECTIVE: **Recognize a fraction as division.**

This is review. Students should be able to explain a fraction several ways, including recognizing the bar line as a symbol for division. The denominator is the divisor, the numerator the dividend. Have them indicate understanding by writing a fraction using traditional division symbols.

$$\frac{3}{4} = 3 \div 4 \quad \text{"three divided by four"}$$

5-6 OBJECTIVE: **Determine divisibility by 2, 3, 5, 9, 10.**

Divisibility refers to a whole number quotient and a remainder of zero (e.g., four is divisible by two).

Divisibility Rules

- A number is divisible by <u>two</u> if its ones digit is an even number: 0, 2, 4, 6, 8.
- A number is divisible by <u>three</u> if the sum of its digits is divisible by 3. E.g., 162. $1 + 6 + 2 = 9$. 9 is divisible by 3. Therefore, 162 is divisible by 3 with no remainder $(162 \div 3 = 54)$.
- A number is divisible by <u>four</u> if the number named by its last 2 digits is divisible by 4.
- A number is divisible by <u>five</u> if its ones digit is zero or five.
- A number is divisible by <u>nine</u> if the sum of its digits is a multiple of 9.
- A number is divisible by <u>ten</u> if its ones digit is zero.

Practice

1. Give students a variety of whole numbers and have them apply a given divisibility rule and state whether that number is divisible or not. This can be combined with numbers being compared in place value lessons. To combine it with the objective of making and using charts, list the numbers in a column, leave a column for the test stated (sum of digits, for example) and a column for students to write yes or no (heading: is it divisible by 9? or whatever number being tested).

2. Have students look for patterns. Is a number divisible by two and by three also divisible by six? Ask several such questions to lead students to the discovery that if a number is divisible by 2 numbers, it is also divisible by the product of those two numbers.

5-6 OBJECTIVE: **Divide with 1-, 2-, and 3-digit divisors, up to 3-digit quotients.**

Practice mentally dividing basic division facts.
Then, mentally divide dividends that are factors multiplied by powers of ten: $35\underline{0} \div 7 = 5\underline{0}$

Review the algorithm (procedure) for division *(page 107)*. Remind students to check quotients by multiplying the divisor times the quotient and adding the remainder to get the dividend. Problems should increase in difficulty.

Review   One-digit divisor: 2- and 3-digit quotients (with and without remainders)
Two-digit divisor: 2- and 3-digit quotients (with and without remainders)

Introduce   Three-digit divisor: 3-digit quotients, with and without remainders.

Possible Errors and Solutions

1. Wrong placement of a digit in the quotient.

Reteach the procedure. Ask where the first digit should be placed. Where should they start? They must look at the digits left to right until there is a number large enough to divide. The first digit in the quotient goes above the place of the smallest of those units. (Have them check their quotients: quotient x divisor + remainder = dividend.)

$$\begin{array}{r} 40 \text{ R } 27 \\ 38\overline{)\,1547} \\ \underline{152} \\ 27 \end{array}$$

Compare the divisor (left to right). Begin with the 1 (thousands): not enough. Look at the hundreds: 15—not enough. Look at the first three numbers—154: more than 38. Guess—about how many groups of 38 in 154? About 4. Write your guess (4) above the 4 in 1547. Remember, each digit in the dividend after that correct guess must have a number above it in the quotient.

  Write problems on graph paper to help children keep numbers aligned.

2. Omitting zeros in the quotient.

Reteach procedure. Remind students that every time they bring down a digit, they must divide. It may be helpful to have them subtract zero, then bring down the next digit. Have them check the quotient. (Multiply the quotient by the divisor, add any remainder to the product. If the answer is not the same number as the dividend, their quotient is wrong.)

$$\begin{array}{r} 1 \\ 48\overline{)\,5087} \\ \underline{-48} \\ 2 \end{array}$$
Divide (50 by 48—1).
Multiply (1 x 48).
Subtract (48 from 50).

$$\begin{array}{r} 1\ 0 \\ 48\overline{)\,5087} \\ \underline{-48}\downarrow \\ 28 \\ \underline{-0} \\ 28 \end{array}$$
Bring down the 8.
Divide. 28 is too small.
Write a zero in the quotient.
Multiply 0 x 48.
Subtract (28 – 0)

$$\begin{array}{r} 1\ 0\ 5 \text{ R } 47 \\ 48\overline{)\,5087} \\ \underline{-48} \\ 28 \\ \underline{-0} \\ 287 \\ \underline{-240} \\ 47 \end{array}$$
Bring down 7.
Divide.
Multiply.
Subtract.

3. Leaving a remainder greater than the divisor.

Reteach procedure. Remind students to change their estimate (guess). A first or even second or third guess isn't always accurate. Be certain to compare the difference after subtracting with the divisor.

5-6 OBJECTIVE: Estimate quotients.

Change the dividend and/or divisor so that they are compatible numbers, then divide. The quotient will be a rounded value. The quotient can be calculated mentally.

Estimate   274 ÷ 5   250 and 5 are compatible   250 ÷ 5 = 50
50 is the rounded quotient of the original number.

29,437 ÷ 6   30,000 and 6 are compatible, their quotient is 5,000, which is the rounded value of the original problem.

TOPIC: **FRACTIONS**

5-6 OBJECTIVE: **Identify a fraction as a shaded region; as a part of a group.**

Check students understanding of fractions by having them write the fraction illustrated, and illustrate a fraction written in symbols and in words. Include mixed numbers, improper fractions.

The shaded portions below represent the numerators. The denominators represent the number of parts in the whole.

 $\dfrac{8}{8}$ $\dfrac{1}{2}$ 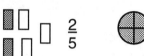 $\dfrac{2}{5}$ $\dfrac{7}{4}$

5-6 OBJECTIVE: **Write an improper fraction as a mixed number and the reverse.**

Improper fraction The numerator is equal to or greater than the denominator: 3/2, 5/5, 23/9

An improper fraction with an equal numerator and denominator represents 1. 2/2, 3/3,12/12

Mixed number A whole number and a fraction. 1½, 12¼, 4¾

Review using illustrations to be certain students understand why a number can be written both ways. For example, 7/4, illustrated above, is also 1¾: students can count fourths, or count wholes and the fraction left.

| Practice |

Have students practice converting without using illustrations.

1. Give students mixed numbers to convert to improper fractions.

    Multiply the denominator times the whole number, then add the numerator—this is the new numerator. 2 ¾ : 4 x 2 + 3 = 11: 11/4. We know this is correct because 11 ÷ 4 = 2¾, the original mixed number.

2. Give students improper fractions to convert to a mixed number (lowest terms).

    Divide the numerator by the denominator, then write the remainder as a fraction: 13/5: 13 ÷ 5 = 2 and remainder 3: $2\dfrac{3}{5}$

5-6 OBJECTIVE: **Identify equivalent fractions.**

Review understanding. Have students prove two fractions are equivalent (same amount of a region or a set) using fraction pieces (parts of a region) and by grouping objects (parts of a set). (Show 1/2 = 2/4) *(Refer to page 111.)*

Review procedure. Give students a fraction and have them write equivalent fractions (multiply the numerator and denominator by the same number). To review the procedure for writing equivalent fractions using cross products, refer to page 146.

5-6 OBJECTIVE: **Write a fraction in lowest terms.**

Review the process.

1. List factors for the numerator and denominator.
2. Identify the *greatest common factor.*
3. Divide both the numerator and the denominator by the greatest common factor.

The **Greatest Common Factor** (GCF) of two numbers is the largest factor that both numbers have in common.

Write $\frac{12}{36}$ *in lowest terms.*

Factors of 12: 1,2,3,4,6,12   *Factors of 36:* 1, 2, 3, 4, 6, 9, 12, 18
Common factors of 12 and 36: 1, 2, 3, 4, 6, 12
The greatest (largest) common factor: 12
Divide the numerator by 12 and the denominator by 12: 12 ÷ 12 = 1; 36 ÷ 12 = 3
Lowest terms: $\frac{1}{3}$

Once students learn to find prime factors, they can use this alternate method of finding the greatest common factor. Write the prime factors of each number, then list the prime factors in common. **The product of the common prime factors will be the greatest common factor.**

Write $\frac{12}{36}$ *in lowest terms.*

Prime factors of 12: 2 x 2 x 3   *Prime factors of 36:* 2 x 2 x 3 x 3
Common prime factors: 2, 2, 3   *Their product:* 2 x 2 x 3 = 12 *(GCF)*

Practice

Have students practice either of these methods:

1. Give them sets of two numbers and have them find the greatest common factor for each set.

2. Give students fractions to reduce to lowest terms.

3. Give the students fractions to reduce or identify as already reduced. When working with fractions, students must be able to determine whether or not their answer is in lowest terms.

5-6 OBJECTIVE: **Compare and order fractions.**

Review   Fractions must have like (same) denominators. If they don't, change fractions to equivalent fractions with like denominators. Then compare the numerators. The relationship of the fractions is the same as that of the numerators.

Compare $\frac{2}{3}$ and $\frac{7}{12}$ $\frac{2}{3} = \frac{8}{12}$ $8 > 7$ therefore $\frac{8}{12} > \frac{7}{12}$ therefore $\frac{2}{3} > \frac{7}{12}$

Order fractions by comparing two at a time.

5-6 OBJECTIVE: **Plot fractions on a number line.**

Plotting fractions on a number line involves comparing and ordering (above), and provides a visual reinforcement of their quantities by placing them in relation to comfortable whole numbers.

5-6 OBJECTIVE: **Add and subtract fractions, mixed numbers.**

Background   Practice finding the least common multiple *(page 161)* to find a common denominator for unlike fractions and reducing a fraction to lowest terms *(pages 112-113)*.

Review with both like and unlike denominators. Remind students that denominators must be alike before adding or subtracting the numerators. Answers should be reduced to lowest terms.

1. Check denominators. If they are not alike, change them to like denominators.

2. Add or subtract the numerators of the fractions. If subtracting, borrow from the whole number if necessary (renaming).

3. Add or subtract the whole numbers if the problem includes mixed numbers.

4. Reduce the answer to lowest terms.

If students have difficulty, reinforce the concept with illustrations.

$$\frac{1}{2} \longrightarrow \frac{3}{6}$$

$$- \frac{1}{3} \longrightarrow - \frac{2}{6}$$
$$\frac{1}{6}$$

$$1\frac{2}{3} \longrightarrow 1\frac{8}{12}$$

$$+ 2\frac{3}{4} \longrightarrow + 2\frac{9}{12}$$
$$3\frac{17}{12} = 4\frac{5}{12}$$

$$6\frac{1}{2} \longrightarrow 6\frac{3}{6} \longrightarrow 5\frac{9}{6}$$

$$- 2\frac{2}{3} \longrightarrow 2\frac{4}{6} \longrightarrow - 2\frac{4}{6}$$
$$3\frac{5}{6}$$

 The least common denominator of two fractions is the same as the least common multiple.

Finding the least common multiple (LCM)

Review the procedure: list multiples of each number and choose the smallest multiple common to both numbers *(page 161)*.

Multiples of 5: 5, 10, 15, 20, 25, 30   Multiples of 15: 15, 30   LCM: 15

Introduce the procedure
Once students are able to prime factor a number, they may use this method to find the LCM: 1. Write the prime factors of each number.
2. List the smallest factorization that contains both prime factorizations.

Find the LCM of 8 and 12.
8: 2 x 2 x 2   **12**: 2 x 2 x 3   2 x 2 x 2 x 3 contains all prime factors of each number: 24

Find the LCM of 9 and 18.
9: 3 x 3   **18**: 2 x 3 x 3   2 x 3 x 3 contains all prime factors of each number.
LCM = 18

Practice

1. Give students sets of two whole numbers to practice finding the LCM. Have them try both methods.

2. Give students sets of two fractions and have them find the LCM for each pair.

3. Have students compare fractions with like and unlike denominators, using =, <, > signs appropriately.

4. Give the students fractions with and without common denominators to add and subtract.

5-6 OBJECTIVE: **Multiply a fraction and a whole number.**

Divide the whole number by the denominator of the fraction.
Multiply that quotient by the numerator of the fraction.

Use illustrations: read $\frac{1}{2}$ x 9 as $\frac{1}{2}$ **of** 9. *Divide* the group of 9 by 2.

⊗ ⊗ ⊗ ⊗
⊗ ⊗ ⊗ ⊗ $\frac{2}{3}$ x 12 = 8
○ ○ ○ ○

$\frac{2}{3}$ of 12

Divide 12 by 3 to find 1/3.
(12 ÷ 3 = 4)
Multiply by 2 to find 2/3.
(4 x 2 = 8)

Remember multiplication is adding like addends. $\frac{1}{2}$ x 9 would be the same as adding

$$\frac{1}{2} + \frac{1}{2} + \frac{1}{2} + \frac{1}{2} + \frac{1}{2} + \frac{1}{2} + \frac{1}{2} + \frac{1}{2} + \frac{1}{2} = 4\frac{1}{2}$$

5-6 OBJECTIVE: **Multiply fractions.**

Use illustrations to develop understanding. Use two different colors in shading, then the portion shaded twice will be a third color and easier to see (yellow and blue = green).

$\frac{2}{3}$ x $\frac{3}{4}$ ⟶ $\frac{2}{3}$ **of** $\frac{3}{4}$ Shade $\frac{3}{4}$ of a rectangle:

Next, divide that rectangle into thirds horizontally ⟶
(because you already shaded it vertically).

Now shade two of those horizontal thirds ($\frac{2}{3}$ of the rectangle).

The portion shaded twice (darker or another color) is the product. $\frac{6}{12}$

After students illustrate and solve several problems using graph paper, ask if they can find the number of squares shaded twice by looking at the numerators in the original problem. *(They have been multiplied).* Ask if they can find the number of squares in the final rectangle by looking at the denominators of the original fraction. *(They have been multiplied.)*

Procedure

1. Multiply the top numbers, multiply the bottom numbers. *(Multiply across.)*
2. Reduce answers to lowest terms. 6/12 in the illustration above would be $\frac{1}{2}$.

To multiply mixed numbers write the mixed number as an improper fraction. Multiply the fractions and reduce the product to lowest terms.

Divide fractions.

Use objects and illustrations to aid understanding.

$2 \div \frac{1}{2}$ means "How many halves are in two?" Divide two wholes into halves.

There are 4 halves.   CHECK:
Therefore, $2 \div \frac{1}{2} = 4$ $4 \times \frac{1}{2} = 2$

$\frac{3}{4} \div \frac{1}{8}$ means "How many eighths in $\frac{3}{4}$?"

If you have fraction bars that can be placed on top of one another (allowing you to see through), place the eighths on top of the fourths and see how many eighths cover $\frac{3}{4}$.

Have students use the fraction pieces or draw illustrations to solve several simple problems.

Solve several division problems. Solve the same problems using multiplication by the reciprocal of the divisor (answers should be the same for each method). Ask the student to find a pattern and draw a conclusion. *Dividing by a fraction is the same as multiplying by that fraction "turned upside down" (or something that describes the numerator and denominator exchanging places).*

(Recripocrals are gray in color.)

$$\frac{1}{2} \div \frac{3}{4} = \frac{4}{6} \qquad \frac{3}{4} \div \frac{5}{8} = \frac{24}{20} = 1\frac{1}{5} \qquad 8 \div 3 = \frac{8}{3} = 2\frac{2}{3}$$

$$\frac{1}{2} \times \frac{4}{3} = \frac{4}{6} \qquad \frac{3}{4} \times \frac{8}{5} = \frac{24}{20} = 1\frac{1}{5} \qquad 8 \times \frac{1}{3} = \frac{8}{3} = 2\frac{2}{3}$$

Reciprocal   Two fractions whose product is one.
($\frac{1}{2}$ and 2; $\frac{3}{4}$ and $\frac{4}{3}$; $1\frac{2}{3}$ and $\frac{3}{5}$)

Procedure   Multiply the dividend by the reciprocal of the divisor.

Why it works

$\frac{1}{3} \div \frac{1}{4}$ can be written $\dfrac{\frac{1}{3}}{\frac{1}{4}}$

In order to have a one on the bottom we can multiply 1/4 by its reciprocal.

But, then we must also multiply the top by that same number.

$$\dfrac{\frac{1}{3} \times \frac{4}{1}}{\frac{1}{4} \times \frac{4}{1}} = \dfrac{\frac{1}{3} \times \frac{4}{1}}{1} = \frac{1}{3} \times \frac{4}{1}$$

(Identity property: One times a number is one. A number divided by itself is one.) $\dfrac{3}{3} = 1$ $\dfrac{\frac{1}{8}}{\frac{1}{8}} = 1$

To multiply mixed numbers write the mixed number as an improper fraction, then divide the fractions.

Watch out for possible errors.

• Changing the wrong fraction. That is, writing the reciprocal of the dividend rather than the divisor.

• Forgetting to write a whole number as a fraction by using one as a denominator. This may lead to confusion in finding a reciprocal or in multiplying across.

Practice

1. Divide fractions and whole numbers by a fraction.

2. Divide mixed numbers by a fraction.

5-6 OBJECTIVE: **Solve word problems involving fractions.**

Use multi-step problems. Strategies should vary: draw a picture, make a list, write an equation.

Of the 36 students in the class, 1/3 bought class rings. One half of the students with class rings also have school sweaters. Those with both class rings and school sweaters will be joining a club that has 15 members. How many members will it have after they join?

To solve

1. Find out how many have rings.   1/3 of 36   1/3 x 36 = 12 students with rings

2. Find 1/2 of that 12.   1/2 x 12 = 6   6 students with both rings and sweaters.

3. Now add those 6 with the 15 members.   6 + 15 = 21 members will be in the club.

5-6 OBJECTIVE: **Write a fraction as a decimal.**

Background   Understand, write, add, and subtract decimals and equivalent fractions.

Begin with a model to illustrate a fraction and equivalent decimal as the same quantity. Since decimals have been illustrated with 10x10 squares, begin with fractions equivalent to hundredths. 1/4 would be 25/100 or a block of 25 squares that can also be seen as 1/4 of the whole. Use examples with denominators of 2, 5, and 10. Students are finding equivalent fractions, and know how to write tenths and hundredths as decimals already; so this should be a simple review.

Next, point out the difficulty of finding thirds or sevenths using graph paper (100 can't be divided by 3 or 7 evenly in order to find equivalent fractions.) *A simple way to find the decimal form of any fraction is to divide the numerator by the denominator.*

Practice

1. Use a calculator to find the decimal form of fractions and mixed numbers.

2. After practice dividing decimals and rounding quotients, divide with paper and pencil, rounding to the nearest hundred.

TOPIC: **ROMAN NUMERALS**

This number system is a contrast to our place value system and is meant to aid understanding of number systems.

5-6 OBJECTIVE: **Identify the value of symbols I, V, X, L, C, D, M**

(No symbol for zero.)	I	V	X	L	C	D	M
	1	5	10	50	100	500	1,000

5-6 OBJECTIVE: **Write the standard number for the Roman numeral.**

Add symbols arranged from greatest to least value:

VII = 5 + 1 + 1 = 7   DCL = 500 + 100 + 50 = 650   LXXI = 50 + 10 + 10 + 1 = 71

Subtract when an I, X, or C is placed in front of a symbol (to its left) of greater value.

CD = 500 - 100 = 400   CM = 1,000 - 100 = 900   XL = 50 - 10 = 40

IX = 10 - 1 = 9   MCMXCIX   (M)1,000 + (CM) 900 + (XC) 90 + (IX) 9 = 1999

(Children may notice Roman numerals in the credits of movies and television shows.)

5-6 OBJECTIVE: **Write the Roman numeral for the standard number.**

Use symbols representing the largest value possible. Do the same for each portion remaining.   623 = D (500) + C (100) + XX (20) + III (3) = DCXXIII

3435 = MMM (3000) + CD (400) + XXX (30) + V (5) = MMMCDXXXV

5-6 OBJECTIVE: **Write a number in standard form in another base system and reverse.**

Studying systems other than base ten helps students understand the concept of place value and, as with Roman numerals, broadens their perspective of symbols and systems. This objective could be met while studying a culture that used another base system (i.e., the Maya), or during a computer lesson discussing the binary system.

1. Use digits 0 through the number one less than the base.
    Base 10: digits 0-9   Base 5: digits 0-4   Base 2 *(binary)*: digits 0-1
    Base 12: digits 0 - 9 and symbols for numbers 10, 11
    (letters of the alphabet, for example. Make a key: 10 = A, 11 = B)

2. Provide a place value chart.
    Right to left: ones, base number, base number², base number³, and so on.
    (Base ten: ones, tens, ten² (10x10 = hundreds), ten³ (10x10x10 = thousands)

Base two	2^4	2^3	2^2	2^1	2^0	Place Value (Place on a chart)
	2x2x2x2	2x2x2	2x2	2	1	(Finding each value)
	16	8	4	2	1	(Value of each place)

3. Write the number with the number of the base system written in small print after the number. 67_{eight} 101011_{two} 312_{four} 401243_{five} 85061_{nine}

Practice

1. Have students write the base ten equivalent of a number in another base system.

    10101_{two} = ? To find the value in base ten, add the value of each place.
    Use the base two chart above to find the value of each place: $16 + 0 + 4 + 0 + 1$
    Add. $10101_{two} = 21$

2. Have students write a base ten number in another base system.

    $422 = ?_{five}$ Make a place value chart for reference: 5^3 5^2 5^1 5^0
    Figure out the value for each place.   5x5x5 5x5 5 1

    125 25 5 1

    Begin with the largest value possible (54, or 625, would be too large). How many
    125s *(5^3)* are in 422? (**3** x 125 = 375 leaving a remainder of 47) How many 25s *(5^2)*
    are in this remainder? (**1** x 25 = 25. 47 – 25 = 22 remainder.)

How many 5s (5^1) are in this remainder? (**4**x5 = 20. 22 – 20 = 2 remainder.)
How many 1s (5^0) are in this remainder? (**2**x 1 = 2)

$422 = 375 + 25 + 20 + 2 = $ (**3** x 125) + (**1**x25) + (**4**x5) + (**2**x1) = (Use the numbers in bold) 3142_{five}

Topic: DECIMALS

5-6 Objective: **Recognize and write decimals to the hundred-thousandths.**

1.   Review tenths and hundredths. *(Refer to pages 115-116.)*

2.   Introduce thousandths.

To help students understand the size relationship, show them the 10 x 10 centimeter square. How many squares are here? *(100)* If I divided each of the hundred squares into ten sections, how many squares would there be? (10 x 100 = 1,000)

Use a place value chart to introduce thousandths. Place numbers in the chart and have students practice reading them. Tell them a number and have them write it or place number cards on the chart. Provide practice with numbers which require a zero to hold a place.

3.   Compare and order decimals to the thousandths before introducing other place values.

5-6 Objective: **Using an illustration, write decimals as fractions, percents, and with words.**

Check students understanding of decimals. When they see a section of a 10 x 10 cm square shaded, they should be able to write it as a decimal, fraction, percent, and with words.

If 25 squares are shaded: 0.25, 25/100 = ¼, 25%, twenty-five hundredths.

If one entire block and 13 squares in another block are shaded: 1.13, 1 13/100, 13%, one and thirteen hundredths.

5-6 Objective: **Compare and order decimals with same and different place values.**

Have students plot decimals on a number line. This helps them visualize their values.

Compare numbers with the same value, reviewing with familiar numbers. Then, remind students how to write equivalent numbers (adding zeros) to compare numbers with different place values. Eventually, students should be able to compare decimals of different place values without lining them up or writing equivalent decimals.

Compare 13.05 and 13.4   13.05 and 13.4<u>0</u> (Zero is added to 13.4 so that both numbers have digits to the hundredths place. Adding zero does not change the value, but may help students who need to line up numbers for comparison.) Numbers are the same until the tenths place. 4 is greater than 0.   13.05 < 13.4

5-6 OBJECTIVE: ## Round to the nearest tenth, hundredth, whole number.

Review the procedure for rounding decimals to the nearest whole number *(pages 117-118)*. Explain that decimals with other place values are rounded the same way:

1. Underline the digit in the place to which you want to round.
2. Look at the digit one place to its right.
3. If that digit is five or more, add one to the underlined digit, and delete everything to its right *(round up)*.
4. If that digit is less than five, don't change the underlined digit, but delete everything to its right *(round down)*.

Unlike whole numbers, rounded decimals do not need to end with zeros. For example, 38 rounded to the nearest ten is 40. But, .38 rounded to the nearest tenth can be written .40 or .4—the zero is not necessary as a place holder.

Don't require students to underline the digit if they can round successfully mentally. This is suggested only as an aid.

to the whole number			to the tenth		to the hundredth	
32.6841	3<u>2</u>.6841	*33.0*	32. <u>6</u>841	*32.7*	32.6<u>8</u>41	*32.68*
5.2159	<u>5</u>.2159	*5.0*	5.<u>2</u>159	*5.2*	5.21<u>5</u>9	*5.216*

5-6 OBJECTIVE: ## Estimate by rounding sums, differences, products, and quotients.

Once students learn how to round, have them practice by rounding numbers to be added, subtracted, multiplied or divided to the nearest whole number and then carry out the operation mentally. 23.54 + 124.71:   24 + 125 = 149

If they have several numbers that vary only slightly, instead of rounding, choose an approximate number to represent each addend: 35.6 + 36.2 + 34.8 + 36.2 would be 35 + 35 + 35 + 35

5-6 OBJECTIVE: **Add and subtract through the hundred-thousandths place.**

Teaching Grades 3-4 introduced adding and subtracting through the hundredths place.

1. Review the procedure *(page 116)* using visual aids—place value blocks, shaded squares of graph paper.

The amount of time spent on review and with aids depends on the needs of the student. For those who think they remember the procedure and would rather solve problems without aids, check for understanding of why the procedure works (let him illustrate with the visual aids). If his understanding is weak, review with the aids, then have him write problems on a place value chart for reinforcement. Use the place value chart as a transition for hands-on learners that may need more experiences to remember place values, *and for initial practice adding and subtracting places through the hundred-thousandths if necessary.*

2. Include problems requiring renaming.

Remind students that the place to the left of a digit is ten times more. (Ten ones is a ten; ten tens is a hundred. Ten tenths is a one; ten hundredths is a tenth; ten thousandths is a hundredth; and so on.) They are always trading 10 for one of the left place, or borrowing ten from the left, even with decimals.

$$\begin{array}{r} 1\ \ 1 \\ 1.46 \\ +\ \ 2.67 \\ \hline \end{array}$$

6 hundredths plus 7 hundredths is 13 hundredths, or one tenth and 3 hundredths.
1 tenth, 4 tenths, plus 6 tenths is 11 tenths, or one and 1 tenth.
1 plus 1 plus 2 is 4
Place the decimal. The sum is 4.13.

3. Students should write in zeros if they are confused by working with numbers with different place values. (1/10 or 0.1 is the same as 10/100 or 0.10 They are equivalent numbers.)

However, at some point, they should recognize place value well enough not to need the zeros.

$$\begin{array}{r} 5.1 \\ -\ 2.35 \\ \hline \end{array} \quad \text{can be written} \quad \begin{array}{r} 5.10 \\ -\ 2.35 \\ \hline \end{array}$$

The Procedure

1. Add or subtract digits in the far right column first. Trade or borrow if necessary.

2. Proceed one digit to the left and add or subtract digits in that column. Trade or borrow.

3. Continue moving one digit to the left until all digits have been added or subtracted.

4. Place the decimal point in the answer. It must line up with the other decimals.

5-6 OBJECTIVE: **Multiply a decimal by a whole number, a power of ten, a decimal.**

Background   Shading in 10 x 10 centimeter squares to represent decimals and finding the area of a rectangle.

Teaching the Concept

Have students read the multiplication sign as "of" and use models to help them understand multiplication involving decimals. 0.5 x 2 would be read "five-tenths of two" or "half of two." Because the product in multiplying with whole numbers greater than one is always more than either factor, students are often confused by multiplication of fractions and decimals.

Following are two common methods for illustrating the concept.

METHOD ONE

1. Outline a 10 x 10 square on graph paper. Review: one row or column represents what decimal? (0.1) Give the students a decimal less than one to illustrate by coloring adjacent *columns*. (0.5: color 5 columns.) Have the students use another color and illustrate the same decimal by coloring adjacent *rows*. (They must understand that rows *or* columns can be used to show the same value.) Students should notice that the intersecting areas are a combination of the two colors. (That new color represents 0.5 of 0.5 or 0.5 x 0.5: **.25**. There should be 25 squares (each representing 1/100) that were colored with both crayons or markers. See #2, below.)

2. Have students use two colors (i.e., yellow and blue) on a 10x10 square to illustrate one decimal times another. Give students a problem using the word *of*, not times. *Color 0.5 of 0.6.* The student uses yellow to color in 0.6 of the large square (6 of the 10 columns of 10 small squares). He now has a rectangle made up of 6 yellow columns of 10 squares each. Then, using blue, he shades in 0.5 of his yellow rectangle—5 rows 6 small squares wide. The area shaded with both colors (green) represents the answer (30 squares representing 1/100 each = .30)

3. Use several 10x10 squares to illustrate problems with decimals greater than one. For example, 0.7 of 3.2. Begin with 4 squares. Using yellow, color 3 of the large 10x10 squares completely and 2 columns of the fourth. Using blue, color in 7 rows of the 3 large squares and 7 rows of the yellow rectangular section in the fourth large square (i.e., 7 rows of 2 small squares each). Count the small squares now colored green by

the overlapping of blue and yellow. There should be 70 small green squares in each of the 3 large squares, totaling 210. There should be 14 small green squares in the 4th large square. The total of small green squares in the 4 large squares is 224. Since each small square represents 1/100 of the large square, we move the decimal point two places to the left to indicate hundreths: **2.24**.

4. Explain that finding the decimal part of another decimal (--of--) is the same as multiplying decimals. 0.7 of 3.2 is 2.24   0.7 x 3.2 = 2.24

METHOD TWO

1. Using graph paper, have students draw rectangles to demonstrate area:

   To form the rectangles they should count down the first factor and across the second.

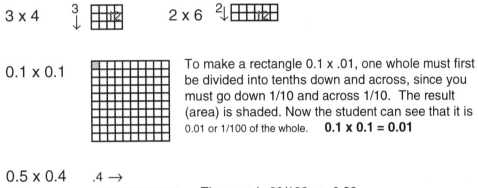

0.5 x 0.4

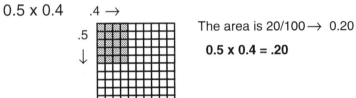

The area is 20/100 → 0.20

0.5 x 0.4 = .20

Teaching the Algorithm (procedure)

Multiplying decimals follows the same procedure as multiplying whole numbers, except for having to place the decimal point. Direct students to discover the pattern that gives them a rule for placing the decimal. *The number of decimal places in the product is determined by adding the number of decimal places in the factors.* (In 0.32 x 0.4 the product will have three places after the decimal point: 0.128.)

Here's one approach to directing students toward discovering that pattern. Explain that they multiply the numbers the same way as they did with whole numbers, but you want them to find a pattern in order to know where to place the decimal point. Let them use a calculator to multiply a list of decimals, recording the answer. Then have them look over the page, underlining the places after the decimal in the factors and in the product. Ask them to find the relationship between the number of decimal places in the factors and in the product. There should be several examples of one, two, three, and four places after the decimal. Include multiplying a decimal by a whole number.

2.3 x 0.50   78 x 0.15   6 x 0.3   19 x 3   9.1 x .36

The Algorithm (procedure)

1. Multiply as with whole numbers.
2. Count the number of places after the decimal in each factor, add them.
   That sum is the number of decimal places in the product.
3. Count from right to left to place the decimal.

Multiply as with whole numbers. Count and add decimal places in both factors. Count places right to left and place the decimal point in the product.

$$
\begin{array}{rl}
4.75 & \rightarrow \quad \text{2 decimal places} \\
\times\ 1.2 & \rightarrow \quad +\ \text{1 decimal place} \\
\hline
9\,5\,0 & \\
47\,5\,0 & \quad \text{3 decimal places} \\
\hline
57\,0\,0 & \rightarrow \boxed{5.70}
\end{array}
$$

Practice

1. Give students problems to practice the procedure on their own, no calculators. Use factors with decimal places to the tenths and hundredths before increasing difficulty. Include problems using a whole number as a factor.

2. Include decimals in measurements of figures for finding perimeter, area, and volume.

5-6 OBJECTIVE: **Multiply a decimal mentally by a power of ten. (10, 100, 1,000)**

Review   Ask students what they do to mentally multiply whole numbers by a power of ten. Attach zeros: 24 x 1<u>0</u> = 24<u>0</u>   24 x 1<u>00</u> = 2,4<u>00</u>   24 x 1,<u>000</u> = 24,<u>000</u>

Ask   Will this work with decimals? Would 6.4 x 10 be 6.40? Why doesn't it work? (Attaching zeros to a decimals doesn't change the amount: 6.40 and 6.400 both equal 6 4/10.) Have students multiply decimals by powers of ten with a calculator, recording each product. Then ask them to find the pattern between the numbers of zeros in 10, 100, and 1,000 and moving the decimal point.

The Rule   Move the decimal point one place to the right per zero in the power of ten.
6.4 x 10 = 64.0   6.4 x 100 = 640.0   6.4 x 1,000 = 6400.0

5-6 OBJECTIVE: **Divide a decimal by a whole number.**

(Grade 6)

Once students are capable of dividing whole numbers, dividing a decimal is just a matter of placing the decimal point straight above its place in the dividend on the answer bar. Solving problems written on graph paper may help keep the digits aligned. Zeros can be added in decimal places at the end of the dividend to carry out division until there is no remainder or until it has been completed to the place value assigned (see rounding quotients below).

Procedure

1. Divide the whole number.
2. Place the decimal point in the quotient.
3. Divide the tenths.
4. Divide the hundreds.
5. Continue dividing each place, moving to the right.

Divide the whole number. Place the decimal in the quotient.	Divide the tenths	Divide the hundredths	Divide the thousandths
$$\begin{array}{r} 0. \\ 37\overline{)\,9.361} \end{array}$$	$$\begin{array}{r} 0.2 \\ 37\overline{)\,9.361} \\ \underline{7\,4} \\ 1\,9 \end{array}$$	$$\begin{array}{r} 0.25 \\ 37\overline{)\,9.361} \\ \underline{7\,4} \\ 1\,96 \\ \underline{1\,85} \\ 11 \end{array}$$	$$\begin{array}{r} 0.253 \\ 37\overline{)\,9.361} \\ \underline{7\,4} \\ 1\,96 \\ \underline{185} \\ 111 \\ \underline{111} \\ 0 \end{array}$$

When dividing decimals students will experience what appear to be never-ending problems because they can add zeros.

A **repeating decimal** repeats a pattern of numbers (or one number). To indicate this without writing it over and over, a line is drawn over the pattern to be repeated.

     .454545 . . . is written $.\overline{45}$ .08333 . . . is written $.08\overline{3}$

A **terminating decimal** will eventually end (reach a point where there is no remainder).

> **Practice**

1. Allow students to use calculators to convert fractions to decimals and write repeating decimals using the line over the repeating pattern.

2. Assign a place value for rounding (to the hundredths, thousandths) for conversion problems using pencil and paper.

5-6 OBJECTIVE: **Divide a decimal by 10, 100, 1,000.**

(Grade 6)

Have students find the pattern and draw a conclusion (make a generalization) that will allow them to divide mentally by 10, 100, or 1,000. Give them several decimals and whole numbers to divide with a calculator by 10, then 100, then 1,000. Record quotients in an orderly way to aid discovery of the pattern.

$2548.3 \div 10$	$= 254.83$	$35 \div 10$	$= 3.5$	$6302.54 \div 10$	$= 630.254$
$2548.3 \div 100$	$= 25.483$	$35 \div 100$	$= 0.35$	$6302.54 \div 100$	$= 63.0254$
$2548.3 \div 1{,}000$	$= 2.5483$	$35 \div 1{,}000$	$= 0.035$	$6302.54 \div 1{,}000$	$= 6.30254$

Ask

1. Where does the decimal move when dividing by 10?   (one place to the left)
2. Where does the decimal move when dividing by 100?   (two places to the left)
3. Where does the decimal move when dividing by 1,000?   (three places to the left)
4. What is the relationship between the number of zeros in the divisor of 10, 100, and 1,000 and the number of places the decimal is moved?
5. The number of zeros is the same as the number of places the decimal is moved to the left?

Rule   Move the decimal one place to the left for every zero in the power of ten.

Have students practice dividing problems mentally (no calculator). If a student has difficulty, write a decimal on a marker board and in an upper corner write 10, 100, 1,000. Point to one of the multiples of ten and have the student erase the decimal point and write it in the proper place. Point to another multiple, have him erase and write in a new decimal point, and so on.

5-6 OBJECTIVE: **Divide a decimal by a decimal.**
Grade 6

Students should first have practice dividing a decimal by a whole number and by powers of ten. Then simply teach the procedure for dividing by a decimal.

1. Change the divisor to a whole number by moving the decimal to the right.

2. Count the number of places you moved the decimal in the divisor, then move the decimal in the dividend the same number of places to the right.

3. Divide using the same procedure as dividing by a whole number.

    Check: divisor times quotient = dividend

Move the decimal point in 0.12 two places to the right to make a whole number.

Then move the decimal point two places in the dividend.

$$0.12\overline{)4.325} \quad \rightarrow \quad 12\overline{)432.5} \quad \text{Then divide.}$$

Why this can be done.

You are multiplying the divisor by a power of ten, and multiplying the dividend by the same power of ten. Recall practice with fractions: 9/3 x 10/10 = 90/30 9/3 = 3 and 90/30 = 3 multiplying by 10 (or a power of ten) <u>did not change the quotient</u>. We can multiply the divisor and the dividend by whatever power of ten will change the divisor to a whole number without changing the quotient. When multiplying a decimal by a power of ten, students discovered a pattern that allowed them to simply move the decimal point to the right the same number of places as the number of zeros in the power of ten, rather than carrying out a long multiplication problem. The procedure for dividing a decimal, then, is a short cut.

5-6 OBJECTIVE: **Round quotients.**

Have students carry out division normally but to one place beyond the place to which they are rounding: the nearest tenth, hundredth, or thousandth. Once division is complete, round the quotient by looking at the last digit. If it is 5 or more, round up (increase the number to its left by one). If the last digit is less than 5, drop it. Unlike whole numbers, a zero does not have to replace the final digit.

Round to the nearest tenth: 345 ÷ 7

```
        49.28
    7) 345.00   ←——— Write zeros one place beyond the
       28              place to which you are rounding.
       65
       63
        20
        14
        60
        56
         4      (Stop here. You don't need more places.)
```

Practice

1. Give students problems to solve with pencil and paper.

2. Combine with the objective of converting fractions to decimals by giving them fractions and letting them use a calculator to find the quotient, then round the quotient to the nearest thousandth.

POSITIVE AND NEGATIVE INTEGERS

5-6 OBJECTIVE: **Understand, identify, and write positive and negative integers.**

Students have used number lines, counting positive integers from zero. Show them negative numbers to the left of zero. (Practice reading thermometers in degrees below zero has provided some background.) Note: Zero is neither positive nor negative, but it is an integer.

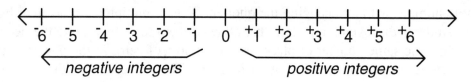

Point out the signs in front of the numbers and explain how the number is read.

-3 is read "negative three." +3 is read "positive three." -3 and +3 are opposites. Each integer has an opposite. They are equal distances from zero in opposite directions.

The opposite of a negative integer is positive. The opposite of a positive integer is negative.

    Once students recognize the positive sign, explain that numbers greater than zero are positive even though written without the sign. Once understood, it is not necessary to write the positive sign in front of the integer.

Practice

1. Have students read various integers.

2. Have students write the opposite of various integers.

3. Provide word problems that apply understanding of the positive and negative concepts by including any of the following opposite expressions:

temperature	above zero / below zero		
money	earn / spend	increase / decrease	profit / loss
weight	gain / lose		

5-6 OBJECTIVE: **Compare and order integers.**

Continue practice to reinforce understanding of integers by having students comparing two integers and arranging 4 or 5 in order from least to greatest. Allow students to use a number line in decision making. The number line does not need to include every number in the practice exercise. Have students use symbols < and > in comparisons.

When comparing, students should realize that numbers on the right on a number line are greater than those to the left, and positive numbers are greater than negative numbers.

$-9 > -12$ (-9 is to the right of -12) $-4 < 2$ (- 4 is to the left of 2)

Remember to order numbers by comparing two at a time.

Order least to greatest -5, 0, -3, 6 →   -5, -3, 0, 6

5-6 OBJECTIVE: **Add and subtract integers using properties of integers.**

Begin with addition.
Have students add using a number line. A positive number requires moving to the right that number of units. A negative number requires moving left that number of units.

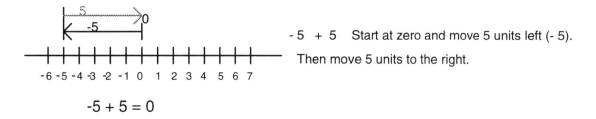

$-5 + 5$ Start at zero and move 5 units left (- 5).
Then move 5 units to the right.

$-5 + 5 = 0$

Have students look for patterns.
- What is the sum of an integer and its opposite? *(zero)*
- Is the sum of two negative numbers positive or negative? *(negative)*
- Is the sum of two positive integers positive or negative? *(positive)*

Introduce subtraction.
Because students have added a negative integer, they can compare that addition to subtraction:
$$6 + (-2) = 4 \text{ and } 6 - 2 = 4 \text{ therefore } 6 + (-2) = 6 - 2$$

Have students practice writing a few simple subtraction problems as addition with a negative integer and solve. Can they draw a conclusion? *To subtract an integer, change the integer to its opposite and add.*

Provide examples of subtraction problems with a negative integer as the number subtracted: $9 - (-4)$ The opposite of (-4) is 4. Add $9 + 4 = 13$

$(-6) - 3$ The opposite of 3 is (-3). Add $(-6) + (-3) = (-9)$

Provide a variety of practice problems.

TOPIC: **ALGEBRA**

5-6 OBJECTIVE: **Evaluate algebraic expressions when given a value for the variable.**

A variable representing one unknown number

Students have had practice adding with missing addend (15 + ? = 25). Explain that the box or question mark in such problems can be replaced with a letter. That letter represents a number and is called a *variable*. They were able to find the value of the variable because they knew both sides of the <u>equation</u> (one side equals the other). If they only had one side of the equation, the side with the variable, it would be called an *algebraic <u>expression</u> (e.g., 15 + t).* (A <u>numerical</u> expression is simply a name for a number: 8 + 2 or 3 x 4, for example.) *To find the value of the algebraic expression 15 + t we must assign a number to the variable (t) then carry out the operation (add).*

Practice

1. Let children practice finding the value of expressions when the variable is given a value and there is only one operation:

   $x + 7$ where $x = 12$ *(19)* $n \div 5$ where $n = 35$ *(7)* $7 - y$ where $y = 3$ *(4)*

   Students should recognize that $n \div 5$ is the same as $\frac{n}{5}$: the bar in a fraction can be read "divided by."

2. Have students express a number relationship with a variable. (This is used in word problems.)

   "Jane is five years older than Bob" would be B + 5 = J (Bob's age plus 5 = Jane's age)

   Use simple expressions that review terms.
   - The product of eight and a number: 8n
   - A number divisible by (or divided by) 2: $n \div 2$
   - The sum of 12 and a number: 12 + n
   - One less than a number: n - 1

3. Have students use a variable in their number sentences for word problems.

4. After students are familiar with "order of operations" include a variable and its value in such problems: $(n + 4) \div 6$ for $n = 8$ *First (8+4) = 12   Then: 12÷6 = 2*

Once students are familiar with positive and negative integers, include negative numbers in the expressions of addition and subtraction: $-n + 4 = 6 \rightarrow -n = 6 - 4$, $-n = 2$, $n = -2$
(Students may need to use a number line for help.)

5-6 OBJECTIVE: **Graph ordered pairs on a grid.**

Pairs of numbers used to name a point on a grid (a *coordinate plane*) are ordered pairs. Marking the point is called *graphing the point*. Begin with a grid that has whole numbers on a horizontal and vertical axis that intersect at point zero. The horizontal number line is referred to as the *x-axis*. The vertical number line is the *y-axis*. The point of intersection (zero) is called the *origin*.

Give the students pairs of whole numbers and have them graph the points (use graph paper for the grid). Coordinate with geometry by having them connect points that form shapes.

Procedure (using only positive numbers)

1. Look at the first number of the pair. It tells you how many units to move to the right of zero on the horizontal axis.

2. Look at the second number of the pair. It tells you how many units to move up. Ordered pair (2,3) would be over 2 and up 3.

3. Draw a point at that spot on the grid.

Below is a graph with ordered pairs (1,3) (2,5) (3,8) (4,3). Students could connect the dots to make a triangle.

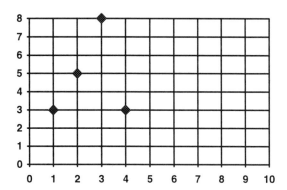

Once students have studied positive and negative integers, they may use a full grid to graph ordered pairs that include both positive and negative integers.

Now the procedure isn't an automatic over (to the right) and up. The first number is "over" but either right of zero (positive integers) or left of zero (negative integers). The second number is "up" only for positive integers, and "down" for negative integers. The point representing (6, -2) would be found by moving 6 units to the right of zero, and 2 units down. A dot would be placed at that point of intersection.

Provide a grid on graph paper and several ordered pairs to be plotted. The intersection of the vertical and horizontal axis is zero.

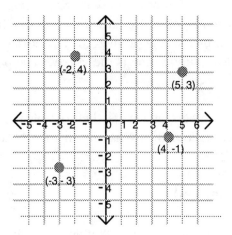

Combine with geometry by having students draw plane figures on the grid, then record the ordered pairs representing each vertex.

TOPIC: # MONEY

5-6 OBJECTIVE: **Add, subtract, multiply, divide by a whole number.**

Include money amounts in general practice exercises with whole numbers and decimals to keep skills polished. Teach multiplication and division of money during decimal units. Provide word problems using money amounts as well.

5-6 OBJECTIVE: **Handle money: count, make change.**

Provide a variety of activities to maintain skills that are necessary for daily life.

1. Using store ads or catalogs, have students estimate items they can purchase with a given amount, then calculate the exact answer. (They could use a calculator.)
    I have $100; I can get 2 of the shirts at $23.95 each and 1 pair of pants for $39.95.

2. Students at this age are often involved in activities that include fund-raising. Let them figure out the money amounts of orders.

3. Suggest students keep a record of money they earn and spend.

4. Provide opportunities for students to calculate and make change. This real-life skill should be mastered.

5-6 OBJECTIVE: **Choose the better buy: unit pricing.**

1. Give students a group price for items and a price for one. Have them determine the price per item at the group rate to determine the best buy.

    Tomato paste on special: 3 cans for $1.00. Single cans of the same size not on special: 49¢ ($1.00 ÷ 3 = 33 1/3¢ per can: the better buy)

2. Combine with review of measurements: give the weight and have students determine price per ounce, pound, gram, or kilogram. Have students compare two items and determine the best buy, comparing the unit prices they've calculated for each. Allow students to use calculators unless practice with division with decimals or money is part of the objective. (Turn a table top into a mini-grocery store. Place boxes and cans with price labels on it for comparison. Students determine the unit price for each and place a tag with the unit price on each item, placing a sticker or drawing a star on the tag of the better buy.)

5-6 OBJECTIVE: **Estimate prices: round to the nearest dollar.**

Have students practice rounding money amounts when practicing rounding decimals. Apply the skill to checking bills or estimating amounts due. This can be combined with practice using tables by having students use menus and estimating the amount that will be due on their (or any) order. Grocery store ads can serve as the source of prices to estimate the amount of money needed to purchase items on a given list.

TOPIC: # TIME

5-6 OBJECTIVE: **Calculate elapsed time.**

Background   Convert units of time.
- hours into days (d) and hours (h)   *(24 hours = 1 day)*
- days and parts of days (hours) into total hours   *(1 day = 24 hours)*
- minutes (min) into hours and minutes *(60 minutes = one hour)*
- hours and minutes into total minutes   *(1 hour = 60 minutes)*
- seconds (s) into minutes and seconds *(60 seconds = one minute)*
- minutes and seconds into total seconds

Example: Convert 200 seconds. Ask: "How many groups of 60 (one minute)?" 200 ÷ 60 = 3 minutes and 20 seconds. (The remainder of 20 remains in seconds.)

Elapsed time is the time between the start and the end of an event. *The meeting began at 9:30 A.M. and ended at 11:00 A.M. How long was the meeting? This can be determined mentally. 9:30 to 10:30 is one hour. 10:30 to 11:00 is one half hour. The time elapsed is 1 and 1/2 hours.*

Introduce writing a subtraction problem to find the elapsed time of an event starting and ending on the same day.

Write the starting and ending times as hours and minutes after midnight so that you are subtracting equivalent numbers. Hours 1 A.M. through 12 P.M. noon already represent this, so write them with the hour given (e.g., 3:57 <u>A.M.</u> is written 3 h 57 min). Hours after 12 P.M. noon must have 12 added to them to show how many hours past midnight they represent (e.g., 3:57 <u>P.M.</u> is written 15 h 57 min). Since 12 A.M. (midnight) is where the day begins, it is the "zero" hour and would be written as such (e.g., 12:57 <u>A.M.</u> is written 0 h 57 min). Now, simply subtract the starting time from the ending time. In a vertical equation, the ending time is written <u>above</u> the starting time.

The field trip bus leaves the school at 10:00 A.M. and returns at 2:45 P.M. How long is the field trip? 2:45 P.M. is after noon. Add 12 hours. It is now 14 hours and 45 minutes.

$$
\begin{array}{r}
\textit{Now subtract} \quad 14\text{ h }45\text{ min} \\
-\ \underline{10\text{ h }\ 0\text{ min}} \\
4\text{ h }45\text{ min}
\end{array}
$$

Renaming is often necessary in order to subtract, or to write answers in lowest terms.

7 h 45 min	3 h 15 min change to:	2 h 75 min	trade 1 hour for 60 min.
+ 2 h 25 min	− 1 h 45 min	− 1 h 45 min	subtract minutes before hours
9 h 70 min = 10 h 10 min		1 h 30 min	

5-6 OBJECTIVE: **Use schedules in problem solving.**

Review time zones Hawaii, Alaska, Pacific, Mountain, Central, Eastern

Have students find out what time it is in several different cities in the United States. They should identify the pattern—the difference in time between zones next to each other is one hour. Looking at a U.S. map divided into time zones with a clock in each section, students should recognize that time decreases by one hour intervals when traveling east to west (and, of course, increases by one hour intervals when traveling west to east).

Apply this knowledge to determining the actual length of time of airline flights from one city to another in a different time zone. Combine with reading tables by providing a flight schedule for students to use as the source of their information.

FLIGHT	*Departure Time*	*Arrival Time*	*Length of Flight*
New York to Los Angeles	8:00 A.M. Eastern	11:00 A.M. Pacific	

Convert the times to the same time zone and solve mentally or using subtraction.

8:00 A.M. Eastern would be 5:00 A.M. Pacific time. From 5:00 A.M. to 11:00 A.M. is 6 hours.

Record the activities and time spent on each in one day (choose any day of the week) and make a circle graph (a "pie") to show the division of your time.

1. Use schedules of transportation arrival and departure times (bus, train, airline) as a reference for word problems. Include time zone references if needed.

TOPIC: **GEOMETRY**

Construct figures using a compass and a ruler. Use models and formulas to solve problems.

5-6 OBJECTIVE: **Identify intersecting, parallel, and perpendicular lines.**

Review
A **line** goes on forever in two directions. What we refer to as lines are **line segments** which have two endpoints. A **ray** is a line with one endpoint, going on forever in one direction. It is written as an arrow with a dot at one end. Two rays with a common endpoint form an angle. *Parallel* lines never intersect. *Perpendicular* lines intersect to form right angles.

Review the symbol for a specific line segment. $\overline{AB}$
The two endpoints are each labeled with a letter. The symbol representing that line is written by drawing a horizontal line over the two endpoint letters.

5-6 OBJECTIVE: **Identify, name, and classify solids according to their properties.**

Have students record observations on a chart so that they can compare information.

Solids (space figures)   triangular, rectangular, and hexagonal prisms; triangular, rectangular, hexagonal pyramids; spheres, cylinders, cones, cubes.

Observe
Number of *Faces* (flat surface)   (F)
Number of *Vertices* (corners)   (V)
Number of *Edges*   (E)
Shape of Faces

Have students draw or trace the <u>different</u> shapes on the flat surfaces of the solid. For example, the top and bottom of a cylinder are identical circles; only one of these need to be drawn or traced.

Practice

Have students compare and contrast space figure models or illustrations.

1. Draw solids on graph paper and/or fold paper patterns to use as illustrations.

2. Identify common characteristics in a given set of solids. Identify contrasts.

3. Put together a set based on a property of their choice to see if other students can identify that common property.

4. Test Euler's formula for prisms and pyramids: $(V + F) - E = 2$
    (number of vertices + number of faces) minus number of edges equals two.

Prisms			**Pyramids**		
triangular prism	rectangular prism	hexagonal prism	triangular pyramid	rectangular pyramid	hexagonal pyramid

Properties to observe

Set of pyramids
- 4 or more faces
- faces are triangles
- bases differ
- named after the shape of the base.

Set of prisms
- 5 or more faces
- faces are polygons
- have two bases congruent, parallel bases
- named after the shape of the base

Compare pyramids and prisms
- both have faces that are polygons
- both are named after the shape of the base

Set of cylinders
- 2 faces (surfaces) that are bases
- bases are congruent, parallel circles
- no vertices
- one curved surface

Set of cones
- one face (surface) that is the base
- base is a circle
- one vertex
- one curved surface*

Compare cylinders and cones
- both have one curved surface
- both have a circle as a base

*To show a cone's surface as a flat shape, take apart a birthday hat and flatten it out.

5-6 OBJECTIVE: **Identify, name, and classify shapes according to their properties.**

Have students record observations on a chart in order to compare and contrast information.

Shapes   circle, triangle, square, rectangle, parallelogram, rhombus, trapezoid, polygons, quadrilaterals

Observe   Number of sides (line segments).
Number of lines that are the same length.
The number of lines that are parallel.
The number of right angles.

A **polygon** is a many- (poly) sided (gon) figure.
A **regular polygon** is a polygon whose sides are all equal in length.
A **quadrilateral** is a four-sided polygon.

By learning definitions of word parts students can define certain polygons.
gon = side   pentagon (5 sides)   hexagon (6 sides)   octagon (8 sides)

Have students define a figure using information from their recorded observations. Parallelograms used for these activities should be like those in the illustrations on the next page. (Squares, rectangles, and rhombuses are also parallelograms because they have opposite sides which are parallel and equal.)

Shape	number of sides	Number of parallel sides	Number: sides same length	number of right angles	Polygon?	Quadrilateral?
Square	4	2 pair*	all (4)	all (4)	Yes	yes
Rectangle	4	2 pair	2 pair	4	Yes	yes
Parallelogram	4	2 pair	2 pair	None	Yes	yes
Trapezoid	4	one pair	None	None	Yes	yes
Rhombus	4	2 pair	all (4)	None	yes	yes

* pair refers to opposite sides

Practice

1. Classify a set of shapes according to a common characteristic.

2. Given a set, find the common characteristic(s).

3. Make a set with a common property for another student to discover.

All sides are the same length: square   rhombus

All right angles: square   rectangle

Two pair of sides are the same length: rectangle   parallelogram

Parallel sides: trapezoid (one pair)   parallelogram (two pair)

Classify triangles by sides and angles.

Triangles have 3 sides, and 3 angles (which total 180°).

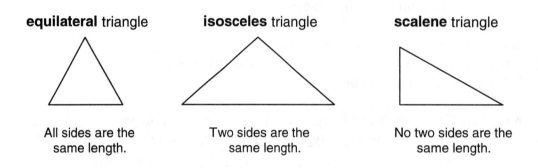

equilateral triangle

All sides are the same length.

isosceles triangle

Two sides are the same length.

scalene triangle

No two sides are the same length.

Help students discover that the sum of the length of the two shorter sides of a triangle must be greater than the length of the third side.

1. Provide three measurements in inches or centimeters.

2. Students draw or construct a triangle with those three lengths.

3. Continue with a variety of measurements for triangles, including measurements that do not fit the rule and, therefore, cannot be formed into a triangle. Students should discover by trial that it is impossible to make a triangle with some of the measurements.

4. Ask students what must be true about the length of the sides in order to draw or construct a triangle.

5-6 OBJECTIVE: **Identify slides, flips, and turns of a figure.**

Plane and space figures should be identified from a variety of viewpoints (top, side views, front, back). Have students slide, flip and turn figures as they make observations. Shapes made on a geoboard are easily turned; cutouts can also be flipped.

5-6 OBJECTIVE: **Identify a figure as congruent, similar, symmetrical.**

Reinforce awareness of shapes by having students identifying whether or not two figures are **congruent** (same size and shape). The figures that are congruent should represent flips, slides, and turns of the original. Then have them make **similar** shapes (same shape, not necessarily the same size). This is easily done with a geoboard.

Observation and study of figures should include observing that figure in a variety of positions (slide, flip, turn) and looking for all possible lines of *symmetry*. Give students cut out shapes that can be folded if necessary. Symmetry means both sides are identical. If the shape is folded in half, sides will match.

A figure can have:

Several lines of symmetry.   **Only one line of symmetry.**   **No line of symmetry.**

Practice

1. Solve measurement problems involving similar shapes (same shape, different size).

2. Provide a shape. Have students measure it and construct a similar shape (larger or smaller).

3. Provide two similar shapes, one with measurements and the other with one measurement missing. Have students figure out the missing measurement. A similar figure may be a flip, turn or slide of the other.

4. Find perimeter, area, length of one side, and/or degree of one angle.

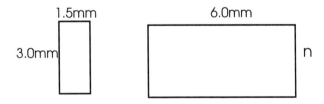

5-6 OBJECTIVE: **Identify, draw, and measure angles in degrees.**

An angle is formed when two rays meet at a point (the vertex). The size of the opening between them is referred to as an angle. The symbol representing an angle requires two things—letters and an angle symbol ($\angle$). Use letters to label a point on each ray and the vertex. The letter of the vertex is always between the other two letters.

$\angle$ABC $\longrightarrow$

Review   Have students identify various angles as greater than or less than a *right angle*.

Introduce   The name for angles that measure greater than a right angle: *obtuse angle*.
The name for angles that measure less than a right angle: *acute angle*.
right angle = 90º   acute angle < 90º   obtuse angle > 90º (and less than 180º)

Practice

1. Have students look at an angle and guess its measurement, then measure in degrees with a protractor.

2. Students should identify the angle measured as right, acute, or obtuse.

3. Ask students the measurement of the angle of a straight line. *(180º)*

4. Give students measurements of angles and have them construct a figure.

By observation students should soon be able to look at an angle and identify it, without measuring, as 45°, 90°, 180°, or 360° (circle). To check, arrange two lines (hands on a clock, two straws) and have students tell you the angle represented.

 Using a protractor to measure angles

1. Place the vertex of the angle on the protractor's center mark (located directly below the 90° mark and halfway between the two 0° marks at each end of the semi-circular scales).

2. Line up one ray on a line between the center mark and one of the 0° marks (which 0° mark used depends on the direction the angle opens).

3. Look at the point at which the other ray intersects the curved scale (rays may need to be extended to cross number marks and single degree marks). Remember that you are reading the numbers from the 0° mark by the first ray, up. Read the closest number where the second ray intersects. If it is not on a numbered mark, count back or forward as the case may be, using the single degree marks along the edge of the arc. Don't be confused by the two scales. One starts at the 0° mark on the left and moves by increments of 10° to the 180° mark on the right. The other scale is just the reverse.

Once students have learned how to measure angles, have them discover the generalization that the angles of a triangle total 180°.

1. Have students measure and record each of the three angles for several triangles then add to find the total degrees in each triangle. To reinforce memory of types of triangles, also require identification of the type of triangle being measured (isosceles, scalene, equilateral).

2. Analyze the above information.
   What are the totals for isosceles triangles? For scalene triangles? For equilateral triangles? What can you conclude about the total number of degrees in any triangle?

3. Provide measurements in degrees. Have students construct angles illustrating each.

5-6 OBJECTIVE: **Construct and bisect angles.**

Bisect means to divide into two equal parts.
When an angle is divided into two equal angles, the new angles are congruent. Students can figure out the degrees of the new angles by dividing the original angle in half.

Procedure
Use a compass and a ruler.

1. Draw an angle with a ruler.
2. Place the point of the compass on the vertex of the angle. (Label it A.)
3. Draw an arc with the compass.
4. Label the point the arc crosses one ray with a letter. (B)
5. Label the point the arc crosses the other ray with a different letter. (C)
6. Place the point of the compass on letter B and draw an arc, then do the same from letter C.
7. Label the intersection of these two arcs. (D)
8. Draw a line from the vertex (A) of the angle to point D. This is the bisecting line.

5-6 OBJECTIVE: **Measure the perimeter of polygons.**

Review   Students have had experience finding perimeter (the distance around) but should keep skills polished. This may be practiced while reinforcing measuring skills by either having students construct a polygon with given lengths, and then finding the perimeter, or having them measure lengths of a given polygon to the nearest fraction of an inch or in metric units.

Have students look for patterns to find possible shortcuts to adding the length of every side. If several sides are the same length, they can multiply that portion and add the rest to the product. A square has four equal sides, so four times one length equals the perimeter. A rectangle has two pairs of equal sides. The student multiplies two times the length and two times the width and adds the products to find the perimeter.

Practice

1. Find the perimeter of a variety of polygons, including rectangle, parallelogram, triangle, and irregular figures.

2. Give students perimeters and have them draw shapes (with a ruler) to illustrate them.

3. Give students perimeters and the number of sides. Have them draw the figure using a ruler. *Telling a student to "draw a 5-sided irregular polygon with a perimeter of 17 units" tests comprehension more than providing drawings with lengths labeled.*

5-6 OBJECTIVE: **Measure the area of polygons using a formula.**

Review   Draw figures on graph paper, allowing students to count squares to find area and to reinforce the understanding that area is always measured in square units (square inch, square feet, square yards). Include figures with irregular shapes.

Introduce the use of formulas.

Rectangles are the easiest shape to use in discovering a way to find the area without counting squares. Have students place squares in a row as the length or base of the rectangle. Then have them place squares in a column at one end as the width or height. Can they predict how many squares will fill the rectangle? (5 rows, 6 in each row. 6+6+6+6+6 or 5x6.) Do this with a few rectangles and ask students for a rule for finding area of a rectangle by multiplying.

Area = length times width (or base times height). **A = bh**

Parallelogram Parts of a region can be rearranged without changing total area. Draw a parallelogram on graph paper and cut it out. Square one side by cutting a straight vertical line. Move that triangular piece to the opposite side. The figure is now a rectangle. What formula could be used to find its area? *(The same formula used for a rectangle, length times width, or base times height.)*

Cut off the triangle on the left and move it to the right.
The base (b) is the length of the rectangle formed.

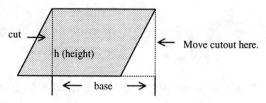

The height of a parallelogram is always a line perpendicular to the base. (It forms a right angle.) Give students base and height measurements to calculate area.

Triangle Use a similar technique to develop the formula for finding the area of a triangle. Cut out two congruent (identical) triangles. Flip one, then place them together to form a parallelogram. It takes two triangles to form a parallelogram whose area is base x height. What part of that total would be the area of one triangle? *(one half)* The formula for the area of a triangle is **A = ½ bh**. Base and height are always perpendicular lines.

If you use right triangles in the demonstration, a rectangle will be formed. This may be easier to understand, but students should recognize that the technique can be used for any triangle.

To find the area of a triangle the student must look for the two lines that are perpendicular (form a right angle) rather than looking at the position of the triangle. When there are no perpendicular lines, draw one from the base to the vertex of the opposite angle.

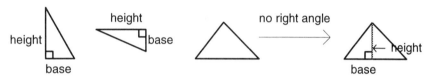

Choose a side to be the base and draw a perpendicular line.

Practice

1. Beginning practice should be with right triangles requiring only the identification of the perpendicular lines to determine the base and height measurements to be used. (Give lengths of all three sides.) Triangles can be drawn on graph paper (or made on a geoboard), base and height recorded, and the formula used for area. But, checking can then be done by counting squares. They can also count squares for the rectangle and divide it in half to check. This provides practice in correctly choosing which lengths to multiply. Rotate triangles so that base lines are not always on the bottom.

2. Using a ruler, draw triangles without right angles on graph paper (or make them on a geoboard). Students choose the base line, draw the perpendicular line, and count units on the graph paper to find the measurement of the height. If they are confused, show them that a rectangle can be drawn around the triangle, using the base as one side, and that the height of the rectangle will touch the point of the triangle. That's the line they are drawing (and measuring).

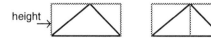

3. Give students a total area and have them construct triangles on graph paper (with a ruler) or a geoboard, recording the base and height of their illustration.

Trapezoid Use the same technique. Place two congruent trapezoids together (one upside down) to form a parallelogram. This parallelogram, unlike the triangles, has two bases, one from each trapezoid. The area of this parallelogram would be (base one + base two) x height. One trapezoid covers half of that area.

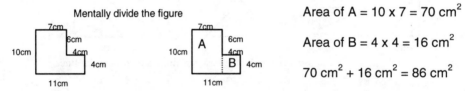

$$A = \frac{1}{2} (b_1 + b_2) \times h$$

Irregular Polygons

1. Break the figure into smaller, square or rectangular parts. Find the area of each part, and add. (Note: cm^2 = square centimeters.)

Mentally divide the figure

Find the area of each part and add.

Area of A = 10 x 7 = 70 cm^2

Area of B = 4 x 4 = 16 cm^2

70 cm^2 + 16 cm^2 = 86 cm^2

2. Find the area of a larger rectangle and subtract the area of the smaller rectangle that represents empty space.

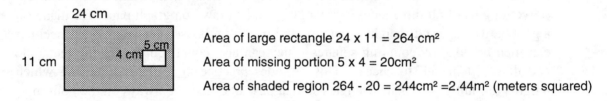

Area of large rectangle 24 x 11 = 264 cm^2

Area of missing portion 5 x 4 = 20cm^2

Area of shaded region 264 - 20 = 244cm^2 =2.44m^2 (meters squared)

Practice

1. Provide practice with area, scale drawings, and converting measurements by using floor plans with spaces for fireplaces, closets and so on as the missing portions.

2. If the length of each side of a figure is doubled, will the area be doubled? Construct models and find out. *(No, although most students will guess "yes.")*

5-6 OBJECTIVE: **Find the volume of a rectangular prism.**

Finding the volume of a rectangular prism is discussed on page 127. Review V = lwh

Practice

1. Give students volume and have them build models.

2. Provide measurements for all three dimensions (use scale drawings) and have students find volume. (Be sure answers are in cubic units of measure.)

3. Have students draw a figure with given measurements for length, width, and height.

5-6 OBJECTIVE: **Find the surface area of a rectangular prism.**

Volume measures cubic units that can fit inside. Surface area refers to the amount of space on the entire surface of a solid. When students wrap a gift they are cutting paper to cover the surface area. Rectangular prisms have flat areas called faces. Surface area can be found by finding the area of each face and adding those products together.

Practice

1. Have students trace the faces of models, measure and calculate the area of each face, then add these areas for total surface area.

2. Provide illustrations with dimensions and have students calculate surface area. Students should recognize parts that are the same size (ends, top, and bottom).

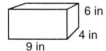 6 in
4 in
9 in

2 ends: 6 x 4 each
top, bottom: 9 x 4 each
front, back: 9 x 6 each

 2cm
21cm   17cm

top, bottom: 21 x 17 each
front, back: 21 x 2 each
2 sides: 17x2 each

3. Provide word problems involving volume.
    If the size of a space figure is doubled (length, width, height), will the volume double? Draw figures, use formulas and find out. *(No)*

5-6 OBJECTIVE: **Find the volume of a cylinder.**

Background   Finding the area of a circle *(page 204)*.

Volume is found by asking two questions:

1. How many cubes will fill one layer? This is the area of the base. A cylinder is the same shape from bottom to top, so every layer will be the same.

2. How many layers will fill the cylinder? The number of layers will be the same as the height.

Volume of a cylinder, then, would be the number of cubes in the first layer times the number of layers. Volume (V) = <u>area</u> of the base (B) times the height (h) **V = Bh**
The base is a circle. The area of a circle = πr^2. The commonly used value for pi (π) is 3.14. To figure out the volume, then multiply πr^2 times the height (V = πr^2h).

Practice

To become secure with the formula, provide measurements for B and h and have students record volume but use a calculator for the actual multiplication.

5-6 OBJECTIVE: **Identify parts of a circle.**

Review   A circle has a center point. The <u>diameter</u> is a straight line drawn from one side of the circle to another, passing through the center point. The <u>radius</u> is a straight line that starts at the center point and ends on the circle. Ask students to find the relationship between the radius and the diameter? *(two times the radius equals the diameter)*

Introduce   A **chord** is a straight line with both endpoints on the circle.

Practice

Give the student a list of diameters and radii. (Use inches and centimeters.) Have him draw circles illustrating each by using a compass.

The point of the compass makes the center point of the circle. The distance from that center point to the pencil point is the radius (that is, how far the compass is open). The student can draw a line the length of the given radius, place the compass point at one end of the line, and the pencil point at the other end. If he is given a diameter, ask him to figure out what to do. (Use the center of the diameter line for the compass point, and one end of the line for the pencil point.)

5-6 OBJECTIVE: **Measure the circumference of a circle using a formula.**

Circumference is the distance around the circle. To understand the formula, students must first understand pi (π).

Have students measure and record the diameter and then the circumference of a variety of circles. They can measure the circumference using a string and measure the portion used with a ruler, or by rolling the circle over a tape measure once. (A dot on the circle's edge would indicate the starting and stopping point.) Ask them to find a relationship between the diameter and the circumference by looking at the ratio $\frac{c}{d}$. (Divide the circumference by the diameter. Answers should cluster around 3.1)

Item	circumference	diameter	c/d

The ratio $\frac{c}{d}$ is the same for all circles. It is called pi (symbol π). $\pi = \frac{c}{d} = 3.14$ or $3\frac{1}{7}$ or $\frac{22}{7}$

Pi is an irrational number. The commonly used amounts above are approximations. To seven decimal places pi would be 3.1415926; however, it actually goes on into infinity.

Using a formula to find circumference:

1. Ask students how to find the circumference if they know the diameter.
   Multiply the diameter times pi.

2. What if we only know the radius? *Two times the radius equals the diameter. So, two times the radius times pi = the circumference.*

Formulas $C = \pi d$ $C = 2\pi r$

Practice

1. Give the students diameters and radii and have them use the formula to find the circumference.

2. Have students estimate and check the circumference of circles, including objects (coin, CD, plate, top of a can).

3. If the diameter of a circle is doubled, what will happen to the circumference?
   (It will also double—back to the idea of a ratio.)

5-6 OBJECTIVE: **Find the area of a circle using a formula.**

Use the basic technique of rearranging pieces to form a shape for which an area can be found. Cut a circle in half, and each half into four wedge shape pieces. Fit the pieces together to make a shape as near a parallelogram as possible. The base of this parallelogram would be πr (half the circumference of the original circle). The height would be r (r = radius). The area of base times height would be πr times r which can be written $A = \pi r^2$.

TOPIC: # MEASUREMENT

5-6 OBJECTIVE: **Read and use abbreviations for units of measurement.**

Refer to page 128 if a review of abbreviations is needed. (Metric abbreviations are also listed on page 205.) Students should be able to read and use abbreviations for all units, and arrange units smallest to largest, or the reverse, within a system.

5-6 OBJECTIVE: **Choose the appropriate unit to use in measuring.**

Review units corresponding to each category, and identify which are metric.

1. Ask students for examples of units of length, weight, capacity, and temperature.
2. Ask students why it is helpful to have different units within a category.
3. Have students arrange units from least to greatest within each category.
4. Have students estimate by using one unit as a reference, then measure several objects. They can visualize more of that unit, or if it is too large, imagine dividing it. Have them decide which unit is the most appropriate for each object.

Measure to the nearest fraction of an inch using a ruler.

1. Record the measurement using a fraction. Write the units. For example: 3¾ cm.
2. Measure a variety of lengths—objects and line segments. Record the measurement. Reduce fractions to lowest terms once this skill has been introduced.

5-6 OBJECTIVE: **Convert measurements within a system.**

Students should practice converting measures in order to compare measurements, and to add, subtract, multiply and divide with units of measurement. Convert units from smaller to larger and from larger to smaller. Knowing the meaning of metric prefixes simplifies this task when using metric units.

Metric prefixes

			(basic unit)			
kilo	hecto	deka	meter	deci	centi	milli
1,000	100	10	liter	0.1	0.01	0.001
			gram			

The values in the metric system are related to the basic unit by powers of ten. Converting from a larger unit to a smaller one requires multiplication by a power of ten, which results in the decimal point moving to the right. Converting from a smaller unit to a larger one requires division by a power of ten, which results in the decimal place moving to the left.

Length				Liquid Capacity				Weight		
*kilo*meter	km	1,000 m		*kilo*liter	kL	1,000 L		*kilo*gram	kg	1,000 g
*hecto*meter	hm	100 m		*hecto*liter	hL	100 L		*hecto*gram	hg	100 g
*deka*meter	dam	10 m		*deka*liter	daL	10 L		*deka*gram	dag	10 g
meter	m	1 m		**liter**	L	1 L		**gram**	g	1 g
*deci*meter	dm	0.1 m		*deci*liter	dL	0.1 L		*deci*gram	dg	0.1 g
*centi*meter	cm	0.01 m		*centi*liter	cL	0.01 L		*centi*gram	cg	0.01 g
*milli*meter	mm	0.001 m		*milli*liter	mL	0.001 L		*milli*gram	mg	0.001 g

Practice estimating and measuring with only the most commonly used units.

Length	kilometer, meter, centimeter, milliliter
Capacity	liter, milliliter
Weight	kilogram, gram, milligram

Practice

Give students problems to convert that require them to multiply or divide. Only after they are secure with procedure, explain that they can move the decimal point.

Lesser amount to greater amount: *divide*

8649 mm = *8.649* m Think: millimeter is a smaller unit than meter. Divide by 1,000.
8649 ÷ 1,000 mm per meter = 8.649 meters

For students with a strong grasp of how multiplying and dividing by powers of ten relates to the placement of the decimal point, allow the use of the shortcut. Dividing by 1,000 means move the decimal point three places to the left.

Greater amount to lesser amount: *multiply*

4.89 m = *489* cm Think: meter is a larger unit than centimeter. Multiply by 100.
4.89 m x 100 cm per meter = 489 cm

Students able to relate multiplication by a power of ten to the placement of a decimal may use the shortcut. Multiplying by 100 would result in moving the decimal two places to the right.

Converting customary units

Length	Capacity	Weight	Volume
12 in = 1 ft	1 gal = 4 qt	16 oz = 1 lb	cubic foot *cu ft or ft³*
3 ft = 1 yd	1 qt = 2 pt	2000 lb = 1 T (ton)	cubic yard *cu yd or yd³*
1760 yd = 1 mi	1 pt = 2 c		
5280 ft = 1 mi	1 c= 8 fl oz		
	1 fl oz = 2 tbsp		

Larger unit to smaller: <u>multiply</u>

5 ft 3 in = ? in	3 yd 2 ft = ? in	4 gal = ? qt
5 ft x 12 *(inches per foot)* = 60 in	3 yd x 3 (ft per yard) = 9 ft	4 gal x 4 (qt per gal)
60 in + 3 in = 63 in	9ft + 2 ft = 11 ft	4 gal = 16 qt
	11 ft x 12 *(inches per foot)* = 132 in	

Smaller unit to larger: <u>divide</u>

63 in = ? ft	28 oz = ? lb	8 pt = ? gal
63 ÷ 12 (inches per foot)	28 ÷ 16 (oz per pound)	8 pt ÷ 2 (pt in qt)
63 in = 5 ft 3 in	28 oz = 1 lb 12 oz	4 qt ÷ 4 (qt in gal) = 1 gal

Convert Temperature

degrees Celsius °C   degrees Fahrenheit °F $\frac{9}{5}$ x °C + 32 = °F

Allow students to use a calculator to convert several temperatures. Students are more familiar with Fahrenheit since that involves their everyday experience. Have them convert several temperatures in degrees Celsius to degrees Fahrenheit. They should make a chart so that they can compare the two temperatures, making a mental association. Students should be aware that writing a temperature below zero requires a minus sign and is read "below zero." Other temperatures are read "above zero." Above zero does not require a plus sign.

Practice

1. Provide problems for conversion.

2. Provide word problems that include measurements.

3. Provide activities that apply learned skills.

Choose the color of carpeting you want for your bedroom. At $21.95 per yard, what will it cost to carpet your bedroom? (Students may measure their bedrooms, or the teacher can provide floor plans.)

5-6 OBJECTIVE: **Estimate, measure and solve problems of length, capacity, volume, weight and temperature.**

Capacity, by usage, refers to the amount of fluid a container can hold (measured in liters in the metric system). Volume refers to cubic units. A solid is cut into cubes, or a liquid is measured in cubic units. When students filled boxes with cubes, they were measuring volume. To estimate, they asked themselves, "How many units will it take to fill this shape?" Students should recognize that cubes can be packed tightly, unlike marbles or other objects, and so make a good choice for finding volume.

Mass refers to the amount of matter and does not change. Weight refers to the force of gravity on an object. Weight varies. A man on the moon weighs less than he does on earth because of the difference in gravitational pull. His mass does not change. However, everyday usage refers to the metric mass measured in grams as weight. Students can be made aware that the term mass may or may not be used on worksheets without going into a lengthy explanation. Instead, focus on helping students develop a sense of the heaviness of metric units by using metric weights and a balance scale.

All metric units should be used for practice converting measures; however only the common units should be used in making estimates. (How many milliliters of cocoa will this mug hold?)

Length   kilometer, meter, centimeter, millimeter
Capacity   liter, milliliter
Weight   kilogram, gram, milligram

5-6 OBJECTIVE: **Use measurements from scale drawings in problem solving.**

1. Students must first practice reading a scale drawing: identifying length, width, height. This can be combined with practice converting measures within a system.
    The floor plan indicates a room 3.52m by 4.25 m.
    How many centimeter long is it?   cm wide?

2. Word problems should use a scale drawing as the source of information. Include maps with a distance scale.

3. Use scale drawings for practice in finding area and volume. (Model homes in new developments have scale drawings available.)

GRADES 7 – 8 OBJECTIVES

Involve Students In
Reasoning
Problem Solving

Provide Opportunity
To use calculators
To program computers

Emphasize
Logic
Real Numbers
Use of formulas

 Items introduced at this level are in italics.

PROBLEM SOLVING

❑   Solve problems requiring 1 through 4 steps.

❑   Use problem solving strategies, including use of formulas.

❑   Solve logic problems.

❑   Use a calculator.

❑   Program a computer.

PROBABILITY

❑   Determine the probability of a single outcome.

❑   Determine the probability of an event.

❑   *Determine the probability of independent events.*

❑   *Determine the probability of dependent events.*

❑   Determine possible outcomes using tree diagrams, tables, *the counting principle.*

❑   *Determine the odds in favor of or against an outcome.*

❑   *Make predictions for outcomes using sampling.*

STATISTICS

□ **Collect, record and/or analyze data including:**

- Bar and double bar graphs.
- Line and *multiple line graphs.*
- *Frequency tables and histograms.*
- Circle graphs, maps, and schedules.

□ **Analyze data using quartile, range, mean, median, and/or mode (statistics).**

□ **Use ratio, proportions and percents.**

RATIO, PROPORTION, PERCENT

□ **Ratio and Proportion**

- Find equal ratios and rates.
- Write ratios as fractions in lowest terms.
- Compare unit rates.
- *Use tangent, sine and cosine ratios to determine length.*
- Solve problems of proportion including applications involving *similar triangles* and use scale drawings and proportions to determine actual measurements.

□ **Percent**

- *Solve word problems involving percent by choosing and solving the appropriate equation.*
- Find the percent of a number.
- *Find the original number when given the percent.*
- *Find the percent one number is of another.*
- *Find the percent of increase or decrease.*
- Find simple interest.

WHOLE NUMBER CONCEPTS AND COMPUTATION

□ **Retain all concepts and skills.**

□ **Read, write, compare, and order numbers through trillions.**

□ **Write numbers in expanded form.**

□ **Add, subtract, multiply, and divide any whole numbers.**

- Divide with three-digit divisors.
- Use divisibility rules to determine divisibility.

❑ **Estimate sums, differences, products, quotients.**

❑ **Identify and use zero, identity, associative, commutative, and distributive properties.**

❑ **Find multiples and least common multiple (L.C.M.).**

❑ **Review factors, prime factors, common factors, greatest common factor.**

❑ **Use prime factors to find the greatest common factor (G.C.F.) of two or three numbers.**

❑ **Write numbers using exponents including zero, one, and negative integers**

FRACTIONS

❑ **Review concepts, practice all skills.**

❑ **Add, subtract, multiply and divide fractions with fractions, mixed numbers, and whole numbers.**

❑ **Find equivalent fractions using cross products.**

❑ **Find the least common multiple.**

❑ **Reduce fractions to lowest terms.**

❑ **Compare and order fractions and mixed numbers.**

❑ **Convert fractions to decimals by division of the numerator by the denominator.**

❑ **Review reciprocal.**

NUMBER BASE SYSTEMS OTHER THAN BASE TEN

❑ Review and practice converting numbers from base 10 to other bases and vice versa.

DECIMALS

❑ Review reading, writing, comparing, and ordering decimals to the hundred-thousandths.

❑ *Write expanded notation of a decimal.*

❑ Add, subtract, multiply, and divide with decimals.

❑ *Write a standard numeral in scientific notation.*

INTEGERS, RATIONALS, IRRATIONALS

❑ Write, compare, and order integers.

❑ *Identify opposite and absolute value of an integer.*

❑ *Memorize and use rules for adding, subtracting, multiplying and dividing integers.*

❑ Use number properties to solve equations using integers.

❑ Graph ordered pairs of integers on a coordinate plane.

❑ *Define, write, compare, and graph real numbers on a number line.*

❑ *Add, subtract, multiply and divide rational numbers.*

❑ *Identify perfect squares to find square roots of positive rational numbers.*

❑ *Approximate square roots of rational numbers to two decimal places.*

❑ Use inverses to evaluate expressions with real number.

ALGEBRA

❑ Write a word phrase as a mathematical expression.

- ❑ **Evaluate mathematical expressions.**

- ❑ **Solve word problems by using equations.**

- ❑ **Simplify expressions using inverse operations.**

- ❑ **Solve equations with one variable.**

- ❑ *Simplify expressions.*

- ❑ *Solve equations involving rational numbers.*

- ❑ *Solve multi-step equations.*

- ❑ *Determine whether inequalities are true or false.*

- ❑ *Solve and graph inequalities.*

- ❑ *Solve and graph equations and systems of equations with two variables.*

- ❑ *Identify ordered pairs as forming a function or not.*

- ❑ *Identify ordered pairs on a coordinate plane.*

MONEY / CONSUMER MATH

- ❑ **Find percents of numbers, the percent one number is of another, the original number when the percent is known.**

- ❑ *Apply percents to calculate simple interest, commissions, discounts, markups, tax rates, percents of change.*

- ❑ *Solve percent problems using equations or proportions.*

- ❑ *Solve problems involving checking accounts, savings accounts, credit cards, purchases, unit rates, best buys, commissions, salaries, overtime pay, budgets, business income, expenses and profits.*

- ❑ *Analyze misleading statistics.*

TIME

- ❑ **Find elapsed time by writing a subtraction problem.**

- ☐ **Use the formula distance = rate x time.**

- ☐ **Retain skill in determining length of trips involving different time zones.**

GEOMETRY

- ☐ **Review definitions of plane, point, line, line segment, ray, angle, perpendicular lines, and parallel lines.**

- ☐ **Construct geometric figures, perpendicular lines, angles, and bisectors using a compass and ruler.**

- ☐ **Classify triangles—right, acute, obtuse, equilateral, isosceles, and scalene.**

- ☐ **Angles**

    - Find the measures of angles using a protractor.
    - Identify a triangle as acute, right, or obtuse according to measures of angles.
    - *Identify angle relationships—complementary, supplementary, adjacent.*
    - *Find the unknown measure of an angle in a figure when given measures of other angles.*
    - *Construct congruent angles.*

- ☐ **Classify polygons, quadrilaterals according to properties.**

- ☐ **Review identification and classification of various prisms and pyramids, cones, cylinders, and spheres according to faces, vertices, and edges.**

- ☐ ***Identify cross sections of solids (space figures).***

- ☐ ***Identify transformations of figures as translation, reflection, rotation.***

- ☐ **Identify symmetry.**

    - Find lines of symmetry.
    - Identify figures as having no line of symmetry.

- ☐ **Solve problems.**

    - Use formulas to find perimeter and area of squares, rectangles, parallelograms, triangles, trapezoids, and circles.
    - *Identify and determine measures of corresponding sides of similar triangles.*

- *Apply the Pythagorean Theorem to solve for missing lengths in a right triangle.*
- *Find the surface area of prisms, pyramids, and cylinders.*
- *Find the volume of cones, pyramids, prisms and cylinders using formulas.*

❑ **Identify congruent polygons and their corresponding parts (lines and angles) by interpreting congruent symbols.**

❑ **Use the rules for congruent angles to determine why two triangles are congruent.**

❑ **Solve for missing parts in a triangle using trigonometric ratio—sin(e), cos(ine), and tan(gent).**

MEASUREMENT

❑ **Identify the more precise measurement.**

❑ **Give the relative accuracy of a given measurement by determining the greatest possible error.**

❑ **Convert metric units of measurement by moving the decimal point.**

❑ **Add and subtract metric units of measurement.**

❑ **Add and subtract U.S. customary units of measurement, converting units within a system.**

❑ **Read thermometers using both positive and negative numbers (Fahrenheit and Celsius).**

❑ **Find the difference between two temperatures in the same scale (Fahrenheit, Celsius).**

❑ **Solve problems involving measurements.**

❑ **Use scale drawings as a source of information for measurement problems.**

TOPIC: **PROBLEM SOLVING**

Review steps in problem solving. If a student has difficulty, it may help to write out and refer to the following list of steps. *(Refer to pages 141-142 as needed.)*

1.	Understand the problem.	*What am I supposed to find out?*
2.	Decide which information to use.	*It is often helpful to write it down.*
3.	Make a plan.	*Which operation will you use first? next?*
4.	Solve the problem.	*Carry out computations for an exact answer.*
5.	Check the answer.	*Is it reasonable? Is it labeled? Check the calculation.*

Continue to solve multi-step problems.

Jane works 40 hours per week at a salary of $5.80 per hour. She earns double time for any hours beyond the 40 (overtime). Last week she worked 43 hours. How much did she earn?

Think. There are several problems here. The salary for one 40 hour week. The hours of overtime worked. The amount earned during overtime. The total amount earned.

1.   40 h x $5.80 = $232.00   salary for one 40 hour week
2.   43 h - 40 h =   3 hours of overtime
3.   3 h x $11.60 = $34.80 earned overtime   ($5.80 x 2 = overtime rate)
4. $232.00 + $34.80 = $266.80 total earned for the week.

Continue practice with mental math strategies.
Count on $26 + $5   count 26, 27, 28, 29, 30, 31

Look for compatible numbers   25 + 46 + 75   Add 25 + 75 first to make 100

Continue use of estimation strategies to determine whether an answer is reasonable.
Use compatible numbers.

Change numbers to rounded or approximate numbers that are more easily computed.
23 + 11 would be 20 + 10 for an estimated value of 30.
2700 ÷ 8   8 is close to 9 and 27 is divisible by 9.   2700 ÷ 9 = 300 as an estimated value.

LOGIC
Use materials that teach specific logic.   Include visual patterns, Venn diagrams, true or false statements, and if - then statements.

PROBABILITY

Continue with activities in which students: *(Refer to pages 143-145 as needed.)*
- List possible outcomes.
- Identify outcomes as equally likely or not equally likely.
- Give the probability of each outcome.
- Record the results.

Introduce the use of formulas.
Have students use tree diagrams *(page 145)* or charts to find the total number of possible outcomes.

Introduce the use of a formula to find the total. <u>The Basic Counting Principle</u> *says that if one thing can be done **n** ways and a second thing can be done in **m** ways, then the two things can be done together in **n** x **m** ways.* Provide activities, some of which involve several stages. Students should apply the counting principle whenever possible.

Several stages: A map with 3 roads from city A to city B, 4 roads from city B to city C, and 2 roads from city C to city D. How many different routes are there from city A to B to C to D? $3 \times 4 \times 2 = 24$

Review simple problems and apply the principle.
Two spinners with three colors, red, yellow, blue. Possible outcomes $3 \times 3 = 9$
3 possibilities on one spinner x 3 possibilities on the second spinner = 9 equally likely outcomes

Chart	RR	RY	RB
	YR	YY	YB
	BR	BY	BB

Permutations are arrangements in a specific order. Combination refers to a set without regard to its order.

If the outcomes are equally likely, use the following formula:

Probability of an event = $\dfrac{\text{number of ways the event can occur}}{\text{total number of possible outcomes}}$

Find probability of independent events using a formula.
When you flip a coin, the probability of heads or tails is equally likely (1/2). When you flip the coin again, the probability of heads or tails remains the same—they are still equally likely (1/2). These are independent events (outcomes). That is, the outcome of each coin toss is not affected by any previous coin toss. If you were to reach into a bag of 3 blocks—one red and two yellow—the probability of choosing red would be 1/3 and the probability of choosing yellow would be 2/3. If you were to reach in a second time (event or outcome #2) the probability of choosing red or yellow would remain the same **only** if you replace the block chosen the first time, making event #2 an independent event.

A formula can be used to find the probability of two independent events (outcomes) occurring: P (A, B) = P (A) x P (B). P is probability, A is one event, and B is the other event. P (A) is the probability of one event occurring, and P (B) is the probability of the other event occurring. P (A, B) can be read "the probability of A followed by B," or "the probability of A then B." Each probability is written as a fraction, so the formula results in two fractions to be multiplied. Using the example of blocks above, the probability of choosing a red block followed by a yellow block (after the red block has been replaced so that they remain independent events) would be written: P (red, yellow) = 1/3 x 2/3 = 3/9 This formula can also be expanded to involve three independent events (outcomes), A. B, and C: P (A,B,C) = P (A) x P (B) x P (C)

A formula can also be used to find the probability of two dependent events. In the example above, if the first block chosen (event 1) is not replaced, the second time a block is chosen (event 2) the probability of choosing red or yellow would be different. If a yellow block was chosen first, and not replaced, only one red and one yellow block would remain in the bag. The probability of choosing a yellow block would now be 1/2, not 2/3, as it was the first time**. The second outcome then, is dependent on the first outcome** (remember, there was one less block in the bag). To find the probability of selecting a red block (1/3) followed by a yellow block (2/2 because when the red block is not replaced 2 yellow blocks remain) could be written P (red, then yellow) = P (red) x P (yellow after red) = 1/3 x 2/2 = 2/6. The formula for finding the probability of one event followed by a dependent event is written P(A, B) = P(A) x P(B/A) where P(B/A) is read "the probability of B given A."

Determining odds
Odds are the ratio of favorable outcomes to unfavorable outcomes. A game show has prizes behind one of three doors. The odds in favor of a contestant choosing the door with the prize is 1 to 2. There is one chance of a favorable outcome to two chances of unfavorable outcomes. If you know the odds, you can find the probability. The total number of outcomes is 3. The probability of a favorable outcome is 1/3. The probability of an unfavorable outcome is 2/3.

Sampling
A random sample of data is used to find probabilities. TV ratings companies poll random sample populations of TV viewers, then use that information to represent an entire population. Since every single TV viewer is not polled, the answers cannot be considered exact. However, the information collected by sampling is considered representative enough to use in making predictions. To find a probability, set up an equivalent equation and solve for the unknown variable.

$$\frac{\text{\# of viewers that chose show A in sample}}{\text{number of viewers in random sample}} = \frac{\text{total \# viewers that chose show A (n)}}{\text{total number of viewers}}$$

$$\frac{112}{1,000} = \frac{n}{1,000,000}$$

$$n = 112,000 \quad (\text{\# that watched Show A})$$

TOPIC: **STATISTICS**

Statistics deals with collecting, organizing, and interpreting numerical data.

7-8 OBJECTIVE: **Find range, mean, median, and mode of given information.**

Continue to provide opportunities to use these skills in analyzing data *(page 143).*

7-8 OBJECTIVE: **Collect, record, and analyze information.**

Continue to use various types of charts and graphs for recording and analyzing information. *(Refer to pages 139-140.)* Graphs can be more complex—double bar graphs, multiple line graphs, circle graphs labeled with percentages or with totals to be written as percentages. *Introduce frequency tables and histograms.*

Frequency tables
Make a frequency table by grouping data into **intervals**. The intervals listed represent the range of values. Intervals should be the same size (called its width). Use tally marks to record scores within the intervals. The number of tally marks for an interval indicates the frequency. If you have a table of information, list the interval or situation to be counted, then count and record the number of times it occurs as Frequency. *To interpret the data on a frequency table, use the following formula and rewrite the fractions as percentages.* Relative frequency equals frequency of interval divided by total of the frequencies.

For example, if a student asked 20 classmates how many brothers and sisters they had, the responses may look like this: 2, 4, 1, 5, 2, 3, 2, 0, 1, 3, 6, 2, 4, 1, 3, 4, 5, 6, 1, 1. An interval would be determined. In this case, an interval width of one sibling will be used. These results could then be recorded on a frequency table.

Number of Brothers and Sisters

Interval	Tally	Frequency	Relative Frequency
0 – 1	I I I I I I	6	6/20 = 30%
2 – 3	I I I I I I I	7	7/20 = 35%
4 – 5	I I I I I	5	5/20 = 25%
6 – 7	I I	2	2/20 = 10%
Total		**20**	**20/20 = 100%**

*A **histogram** is a bar graph without space between the bars that shows frequencies. Frequencies are represented on the vertical axis, the intervals (range of information) are represented on the horizontal axis.* The information from the example above could be recorded on a histogram:

Histogram

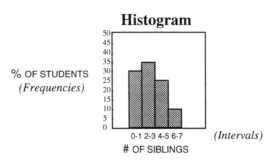

% OF STUDENTS
(Frequencies)

(Intervals)

0-1 2-3 4-5 6-7
OF SIBLINGS

7-8 OBJECTIVE: **Analyze data.**
(Refer to pages 139-143 as needed.)

1. Include consumer information in coordination with a study of money—profits, income over a period of years, frequency of particular models sold, and so on.

2. Find range, mean, median, and/or mode of data.

3. Have students interpret information from a variety of graphs. Ask if the type of graph used for the information is the best choice and why. This will help them in choosing the best format for graphing data which they collect.

TOPIC: # RATIO, PROPORTION, PERCENT

Ratio

Review ratio as a comparison of two numbers or quantities *(pages 144-145).* When written as a fraction it is not reduced to a mixed number. Students should write equivalent ratios and write ratios in lowest terms. 100/10 would be written 10/1 not 10. Since 10/1 is read "10 to 1," this should help students recognize that both numbers are necessary to express a relationship. *(Refer to page 237 for use of tangent, sine and cosine ratios.)*

Introduce Rate

A ratio that compares different kinds of quantities is called a rate. It is most often written per unit or as a quantity to one ratio. This is unit rate. Students have solved problems using unit rates without using the term. Finding out the cost of 3 kites at a cost of $2.25 for each kite used the unit rate of $2.25 per kite.

Practice

1. Solve simple word problems using various common unit rates. (Include problems that allow the use of the formula distance = rate x time.)
   unit rates   miles per hour, dollars per item, words per minute

2. Have students find unit prices for a variety of grocery items.
   per ounce, per pound, per yard

Proportion

1. Review proportion as two equal ratios *(pages 145-146)*. For example, 40/20 = 2/1 (also written 40:20 = 2:1) are equal ratios. Read "40 is to 20 as 2 is to 1."

2. Continue to solve problems of proportion by finding the equivalent fraction or using cross products. (To review equivalent fractions see page 167 and/or 111.)

Using equivalent fractions

$$\frac{9}{3} = \frac{x}{12} \qquad \frac{9}{3} = \frac{9 \times 4}{3 \times 4} = \frac{36}{12}$$

so, **x = 36**

Using cross products

$$\frac{9}{3} \diagdown \frac{m}{12} \qquad 3m = 9 \times 12$$

$$\frac{3m}{3} = \frac{108}{3}$$

$$\frac{3m}{3} = \frac{3}{3}m = 1m = m \quad \Big| \quad \frac{108}{3} = 108 \div 3 = 36$$

$$m = 36$$

3. Use scale drawings to find actual measurements. The scale is the ratio of measurements on the drawing to the corresponding measurements on the actual object. A scale of 1 cm: 3m would indicate that a one centimeter line on a drawing represents a 3 meter length on the actual object. The proportion would be 1/3 = drawn measure (cm)/actual measure (m). The actual measurement (e.g., the length of a particular room) would be the unknown. Use cross products to find the actual measurement.

4. Refer to the topic *Geometry* for explanations of similar triangles *(page 236)*. Use proportions to find unknown lengths and angles.

Percent

Review *(Refer to pages 147 – 150 as needed.)*

1. Percent is a ratio of a number to 100. Students should be able to identify shaded areas of a grid of 100 squares as a percent.

2. Write a percent as a decimal: move the decimal point two places to the left. Convert a decimal to a percent: move the decimal two places to the right.
   23.4% = 0 .234   4.45 = 445%   7% = 0.07   0.03 = 3%

3. Write percents as fractions.
   Write the number as a ratio to 100 (denominator of 100). Reduce to lowest terms.
   22% = 22/100 reduced to lowest terms 11/50

Introduce conversion of percents that include fractions or decimals.

$33 \frac{1}{3} \% \quad \rightarrow \quad \dfrac{33\frac{1}{3}}{100} \quad \rightarrow \quad 33\frac{1}{3} \div 100 = \quad \dfrac{\cancel{100}}{3} \times \dfrac{1}{\cancel{100}} = \dfrac{1}{3}$

$13.9 \% \quad \rightarrow \quad \dfrac{13.9}{100} \quad \rightarrow \quad \dfrac{139}{1000}$

(If students have difficulty converting a mixed number to a fraction, see page 166. In the example above 33 1/3 = 100/3 because 33 = 99/3 plus 1/3 = 100/3.)

7-8 OBJECTIVE: **Solve word problems by choosing and solving the appropriate equation.**

Equations will be based on one of these three problems.
- What number is __% of ___?   What number is 25% of 80?   0.25 x 80 = n
- What percent of __ is ___?   What percent of 80 is 20?   p x 80 = 20
- ___% of what number is ____?   30% of what number is 15?   0.30 x n = 15

See below for instructions in solving each type of problem. Once students have practiced each type, mix problems to check understanding and provide application of all skills.

7-8 OBJECTIVE: **Find the percent of a number.**
What number is___% of___?

To find the percent of a number, change the percent to a decimal or to a fraction and use it to multiply the number. *What number is 75% of 200?*
75% of 200 = 0.75 x 200 = 150   75% of 200 = 3/4 x 200 = 600/4 = 150

Apply this skill to finding tax rates. A sales tax of 7% of the purchase price, for example.

7-8 OBJECTIVE: **Given the percent, find the original number.**
___% of what number is___?

Write the % as a decimal. Use a variable (n) for the original number.
percent times *n* = known amount

50% of what number is 32? 0.50 x n = 32 (Divide both sides by 0.50) n = 32 ÷ 0.50   n = 16

Background Students should be able to divide with decimal divisors.

Explanation 25% of some number is 15. What is the number? We know that 25% becomes 0.25 to find the percent of a number, and we know the final result is 15. What we must find is the original number. Write the equation with the information you do know: 0.25 x n = 15 (n = the unknown number)

To solve, divide both sides by the decimal so that n will be alone on one side of the equation. Recall the use of inverse operations. Division undoes multiplication. Think: Because I want the variable alone, I need to get rid of the 0.25. A number divided by itself is one. Any number times one is that number. What I do to one side of the equation, I must do to the other side. I must divide 15 by 0.25.

$$.25 \times n = 15 \qquad .25\overline{)15.00} \qquad 25\overline{)1500}$$

$$\frac{.25}{.25} \times n = \frac{15}{.25}$$

$$1 \times n = 15 \div .25$$

$$n = 60$$

7-8 OBJECTIVE: **Find the percent one number is of another.**
-- is what percent of ---?

To understand what is being asked, introduce the concept with a situation.
There are 25 marbles in the jar. 5 are blue. What percent of the marbles are blue?

The students should recognize that the percent is represented by 5/25 because of practice with ratios and fractions. In this example they could easily write an equivalent fraction in hundredths to find the decimal, then write the decimal as a percent.

$$\frac{5}{25} = \frac{20}{100} = 0.20 = 20\%$$

The following formula may seem confusing. If so, simply practice with numbers that can be written with fractions using 100 as a denominator for easy conversion. The formula can wait until students have had more practice with algebra.

The Formula
What percent of 60 is 15? Use p as the unknown percent. Students should recall that they found the percent of a number by multiplying the percent (as a decimal) times the number.

$$p \times 60 = 15$$

Divide 60 by 60 to get one (which leaves p). What is done on one side of the equal sign must be done on the other side. Divide 15 by 60.

$$p = \frac{15}{60}$$

Write this as a decimal, then convert the decimal to percent: 15/60 = 0.25 = 25%
(Convert the fraction to a decimal by dividing the numerator by the denominator.)

Find the percent of increase or decrease.

When a quantity increases or decreases, the percent of that change can be found by using the following formula:

$$\text{Percent of change} = \frac{\text{amount of change}}{\text{original amount}}$$

Give students numbers for the original amount and the new amount. Have them find the percent of increase or decrease using the formula.

original amount: 50	*84 to 126*
new amount: 20	The change is an increase of 42.
The change is a decrease.	Percent change = 42/84 = 1/2 = 50%
The change is 50 - 20 or 30.	50% increase
Percent change = 30/50 = 0.60 = 60% decrease.	

Have students apply this skill to word problems involving markups and discounts.

7-8 OBJECTIVE: **Find simple interest.**

Review   Have students use the formula for finding interest.
Interest = principle times rate times time   **I = p x r x t**

(Principle was referred to as "money amount" in *Teaching Grades 5-6*, page 150.)

Give students amounts for each variable and have them use the formula to find the interest. Remember, time must be written in relation to one year. Fractions or decimals should be used for portions of a year. *2 and one half years = 2.5 3 months = 3/12 = 1/4 or 0.25*

TOPIC: # WHOLE NUMBER CONCEPTS AND COMPUTATION

Students should be able to read numbers and identify place value through trillions quickly. If not, review. If computation skills have not been mastered, review, otherwise provide occasional practice to keep skills polished, including division by three-digit divisors. Allow students to use a calculator when high numbers are involved in problem solving situations. Students should recognize and use basic properties (associative, commutative, distributive, identity). Review as needed.

Remind students that addition and subtraction are inverse operations and multiplication and division are inverse operations. (One operation "undoes" the other.) This will help them solve equations with variables.

Begin with x	add five	x + 5	inverse of add, subtract 5	x + 5 - 5 = x
Begin with n	divide by 3	x ÷ 3	inverse of divide, multiply by 3	n ÷ 3 x 3 = n

7-8 OBJECTIVE: **Use prime factors to find the greatest common factor.**

Review   Factors, prime factors, common factors, and greatest common factor. Identify a number as prime or composite. *(Refer to page 160.)*

The greatest common factor can be found by using prime factors.

1. List the prime factors of each number.
2. List all factors in common.
3. Their product is the GCF.

$72 = 2 \times 2 \times 2 \times 3 \times 3 = 2^3 \times 3^2$ Common factors: $2 \times 2 \times 3$ or $2^2 \times 3$
$60 = 2 \times 2 \times 3 \times 5$ $= 2^2 \times 3 \times 5$ $2^2 \times 3 = 12$, so the GCF $= 12$

7-8 OBJECTIVE: **Write numbers using exponents including zero, one, and negative integers.**

Review   Use of exponents *(pages 158, 160).*

Introduce   Negative integers and zero as exponents.

If n represents any number except zero, then n to the zero power is one. $n^0 = 1$

$$n^{-2} = \frac{1}{n^2} \qquad n^{-a} = \frac{1}{n^a} \qquad 10^{-1} = \frac{1}{10^1} = 0.1$$

7-8 OBJECTIVE: **Solve number expressions using the order of operations.**

Review   1. Compute inside parentheses.
2. Do all multiplication and division, left to right.
3. Do all addition and subtraction, left to right.

Give students problems to solve requiring them to use the order of operations. The order should be memorized: "**M**y **D**ear **A**unt **S**ally"— **M**ultiply, **D**ivide, **A**dd, **S**ubtract.

$10 - (16 - 4 \times 3) = ?$ Solve within parentheses first.
$10 - (16 - 12)$ Inside parentheses, multiply before subtracting.
$10 - (4) = 6$

Provide problems with numbers, a total, and a note to indicate which operations are used and how many times each. Have students solve by filling in operations to make the equation true.

6   5   12   6   2 = 5   Use each sign once: +, -, x, ÷.   *(6x5) - 12 ÷ 6+ 2 = 5*

TOPIC:	# FRACTIONS

Review
- ◆ Add, subtract, multiply, and divide fractions with fractions, mixed numbers, and whole numbers. *(Refer to pages 166, 168, 170-172.)*
- ◆ Find equivalent fractions using cross products *(page 146)*.
- ◆ Find least common multiples *(page 169)*.
- ◆ Reduce fractions to lowest terms *(page 167)*.
- ◆ Compare and order fractions and mixed numbers *(page 168)*.
- ◆ Convert fractions to decimals by dividing the numerator by the denominator *(page 172)*.
- ◆ Review reciprocal *(page 171)*.

TOPIC:	# NUMBER BASE SYSTEMS OTHER THAN BASE TEN

Continue practice writing numbers in other bases and converting from another base to our own. *(Refer to page 174 as needed.)*

TOPIC:	# DECIMALS

7-8 OBJECTIVE: **Read, write, compare, and order decimals to the hundred-thousandths.**

Review   Place value to hundred thousandths *(pages 115-116, 175)*.

Have students identify the value of any digit in a decimal in words or fraction form.

$$3.06\underline{7}01 \qquad \frac{7}{1,000} \quad or \quad seven \ thousandths$$

Check understanding of quantity by having students compare and order decimals.

7-8 OBJECTIVE: **Write expanded notation of a decimal.**

Introduce expanded notation of decimals.
Decimal place values are represented with decimals 0.1, 0.01, 0.001 and so on.

$$23.456 \text{ would be } (2 \times 10) + (3 \times 1) + (4 \times 0.1) + (5. \times 0.01) + (6 \times 0.001)$$

7-8 OBJECTIVE: **Add, subtract, multiply, and divide with decimals.**

Continue practice problems to keep skills polished. *(Refer to pages 177-183.)*

Review

1. A line drawn over a digit (or several digits) with a decimal place value indicates that it repeats. $7 \div 9 = 0.7777\ldots$ which can be written $0.\overline{7}$

2. The decimal can be repositioned when multiplying and dividing by powers of ten.

    To multiply, move the decimal to the *right* the same number of places as zeros in the power of ten. Insert zeros as needed.

    $$
    \begin{aligned}
    2.34 \times 10 &= 23.4 \\
    2.34 \times 100 &= 234 \\
    2.34 \times 1{,}000 &= 2340
    \end{aligned}
    $$

    To divide, move the decimal to the *left* the same number of places as zeros in the power of ten. Insert zeros as needed.

    $$
    \begin{aligned}
    2.34 \div 10 &= 0.234 \\
    2.34 \div 100 &= 0.0234 \\
    2.34 \div 1{,}000 &= 0.00234
    \end{aligned}
    $$

3. Divisibility Rules. Apply them to numbers to determine whether a number is divisible by 2, 3, 5, 9, or 10. *(Refer to page 163 as needed.)*

7-8 OBJECTIVE: **Write a standard numeral in scientific notation.**

Review   The use of exponents as writing a number in shorter form *(p.160)*. The exponent tells how many times a factor is repeated and is read as "to the ___ power." $4 \times 4 \times 4 \times 4 \times 4 = 4^5$ (Read 4 to the fifth power.)

Scientific notation uses powers of ten. A number is written as a decimal greater than zero, but less than ten which is multiplied by a power of ten.

1,435 would be written 1.435×10^3 2.4×10^2 represents 240.

TOPIC: # INTEGERS, RATIONALS, IRRATIONALS

INTEGERS

Review   Positive and negative integers and properties for addition and subtraction. Compare and order integers. Find the opposite of an integer. *(Refer to pages 184-185 as needed.)*

The opposite is called the additive inverse. The sum of a number and its opposite is zero.

$$6 + (-6) = 0 \qquad -11 + 11 = 0 \qquad 23 + (-23) = 0$$

Introduce   Absolute value and properties for multiplication and division.

Absolute value of a number is the actual distance an integer is from zero. (Use a number line to aid understanding.) Since the integer -3 is <u>3</u> units away from zero, the absolute value is <u>3</u>. Therefore, the absolute values are always positive, and opposite numbers have the same absolute value.

The absolute value for 3 and its opposite -3 is 3.   Write: $|3| = 3$ and $|-3| = 3$

Give students a few mental math problems using absolute values to check understanding.

$|-20| \div |5| = ?$ *(4)* $7 - |-3| = ?$ *(4)* $|-7| \times |-5| = ?$ *(35)*

The basic properties for addition and multiplication apply to integers (i.e., the *zero, identity, associative, commutative, and distributive properties, pages 94, 100, 142.)*

Rules to be memorized

positive + positive = positive   negative + negative = negative
positive x positive = positive   negative x negative = positive
positive ÷ positive = positive   negative ÷ negative = positive

positive ÷ negative = negative
positive x negative = negative
negative ÷ positive = negative
negative x positive = negative
Any integer times zero is zero

Practice

1. Find the absolute value of integers.
2. Compare and order integers.
3. Add, subtract, multiply and divide integers.
4. Solve equations involving variables and integers.

RATIONALS, IRRATIONALS

Rational and irrational numbers are called real numbers.
Irrational numbers are decimals that do not repeat, and do not terminate (e.g., pi, square root of 5).

Rational numbers are positive and negative fractions.
Like integers, each rational number has an opposite, called the additive inverse.
The sum of two opposite numbers is zero *(opposites property):* $-\frac{1}{2} + \frac{1}{2} = 0$

•   The basic properties for addition and multiplication apply to real numbers *(i.e., zero, identity, associative, commutative, and distributive properties).*

- The rules for adding, subtracting, multiplying and dividing positive and negative integers apply to rational numbers.

Squares and Square Roots

Students are familiar with finding the area of a square by multiplying two identical factors. A square with an area of 9 square centimeters has sides 3 centimeters in length. 3 cm x 3 cm = 3^2 = 9 cm² Three is the number that when squared equals nine. 3 is the square root of nine.

To find the square root of a number n, the student must ask himself "what number multiplied by itself equals n?" The square root of 25 is 5 because 5 times itself is 25.

The symbol for square root is a radical sign which is read "square root of." It denotes only positive square roots. To find the negative square root, place a negative symbol in front of the radical sign. The negative square root of 25 is -5. *A negative times a negative is positive. -5 x -5 = 25*

$$\sqrt{36} = 6$$
$$-\sqrt{36} = -6$$

Have students use the square and square root keys to find squares and square roots of rational numbers with a calculator.

Estimate the range of a square root of a number n. Think of a whole number squared that is close to the number n. Look for squares on either side (low and high) of n. For example, estimate the range for 23. Think: "I know 4x4 is 16 and 5x5 is 25. The number 23 is in between 16 and 25, so the square root would be between 4 and 5."

Approximate square roots by finding a positive integer whose square is close to the number. Divide the number by that integer, rounding to the nearest tenth. Add the divisor to that quotient and divide their sum by two. This method is called *divide and average.*

$$\sqrt{28} \quad \rightarrow \quad 5^2 = 25 \quad \rightarrow \quad 28 \div 5 = 5.6 \quad \rightarrow \quad \frac{5.6 + 5}{2} = 5.3$$

Practice

1. Compare, order and plot rational numbers on a number line.
2. Add, subtract, multiply, and divide rational numbers.
3. Find squares and square roots with a calculator.
4. Estimate the range for a square root.
5. Find approximate square roots using the *divide and average* method.
6. Plot real numbers on a number line.

TOPIC: **ALGEBRA**

Review *(Refer to pages 186-187 as needed.)*

1. Write a mathematical expression for a word phrase.

    6 more than a number $\rightarrow$ n + 6   three less than half of a number $\rightarrow$ $\frac{n}{2}$ - 3

    Use this skill to write equations for word problems. Then solve the equations.

2. Evaluate algebraic expressions.
    Give values for variables and have students evaluate expressions.
    Include several operations. *(Students must use the order of operations.)*

Once rational numbers have been discussed, include rational numbers as values for the variable.

a = 5   a + 17 = ?   (22)   b ÷ 12   for b = 36   (3)   s x 5 + (4 ÷ 2) for s = 8   (42)

7-8 OBJECTIVE: **Solve multi-step equations.**

Solve equations involving one operation.
Have students find the value of the variable (the *solution*) in an equation by adding, subtracting, multiplying, or dividing with the same number on both sides of the equation. When the same thing is done to both sides, the equations will be equivalent. What they choose to do depends on what operations are used with the variable. They want to get the variable alone on one side and its value on the other. If a number is subtracted from the variable, adding that same number will get rid of it (*inverse operations.*) But, what is done to one side of the equation must be done to the other so that they are equivalent (same operation, same number).

n + 7 = 12   *inverse operation: subtraction*   4c = 36 *to get c alone, use the inverse operation*
n + 7 − 7 = 12 − 7 *[7+ (−7) = 0; n+ 0 = n]* $\frac{4c}{4}$ = $\frac{36}{4}$ *(4 ÷ 4 = 1 1c = c)*
n = 5   c = 9

t − 13 = −3 $\frac{w}{6}$ = 12   *inverse operation, multiply*
t − 13 + *13* = −3 + *13*
t = 10   6 ($\frac{w}{6}$) =   6 (12)

                                                              w = 72

Practice

1. Solve a variety of equations with variables using the procedure above.
2. Once rational numbers have been discussed, solve equations which include rational numbers.

Solve equations involving more than one operation.

The goal is the same—to get the variable alone on one side. Follow the same procedure as above. It is usually simplest to add or subtract first, then multiply or divide.

$$3p - 5 = 46$$
$$3p - 5 + 5 = 46 + 5$$
$$3p = 51$$
$$\frac{3p}{3} = \frac{51}{3}$$
$$p = 17$$

Practice

1. Solve a variety of equations.
2. Write an equation with a variable when solving word problems.

7-8 OBJECTIVE: **Identify ordered pairs as forming a function or not.**

Introduce variables that are related to each other. $x + 4 = y$
The value of y depends on the number substituted for x. When each value of x has only one value of y, the ordered pair forms a *function*. If two ordered pairs in the set have the same value for x and a different value for y, the relation would *not* be a function. If the relation between x and y is an inequality *less than* $(x < y)$ the relation will *not* be a function because several ordered pairs in the set can have the same value of x and a variety of values for y. (2,3) (2,4) (2,5) and so on. Students have had experience with graphing given ordered pairs, now they will find ordered pairs.

Provide an equation using two variables. Have students find several ordered pairs by making a chart. Give them values for either x or y to find the value of the other variable, or have them choose any value for x and then find y. Use positive and negative integers. Ask students if the set of ordered pairs forms a function.

$x - 2 = y$

x	y	(x, y)
0	-2	(0, -2)
4	2	(4, 2)
-3	-5	(-3, -5)
-5	-7	(-5, -7)

$4m = n$

m	n	(m, n)
0	0	(0, 0)
1	4	(1, 4)
2	8	(2, 8)
3	12	(3, 12)

$c = d \div 2$

c	d	(c, d)
1	2	(1, 2)
-2	-4	(-2, -4)
6	12	(6, 12)
-6	-12	(-6, -12)

Numbers to be filled in by students are in **boldface.**

7-8 OBJECTIVE: **Solve and graph equations and systems of equations with two variables.**

Students have practiced plotting ordered pairs. Explain that the grid is called the *coordinate plane* and ordered pairs are *coordinates.* The horizontal number line is called the *x-axis* and the vertical number line is the *y-axis.* Each point in the plane is named by a pair of coordinates (ordered pair) which tell how far that point is from the **origin** (the zero, or point of intersection of the x-axis and y-axis) and in what direction.

When using two number lines of real numbers (positive, negative), the plane has four **quadrants.**

Quadrant I   (x,y) (right, up)   **Quadrant II** (-x,y) (left, up)
Quadrant III (-x,-y) (left, down)   **Quadrant IV** (x, -y) (right, down)

Points that fall directly on an axis are not in any quadrant.

Systems of Equations

Two equations with the same variables form a system of equations. An ordered pair that is a solution for both equations is the solution of the **system.**

$$x + y = 26 \quad \text{and} \quad x - y = 8 \quad \text{represent a system of equations}$$

To find the solution of the system, graph ordered pairs for each equation. If the graphs intersect, the coordinates of the point of intersection are the solution of the system.

Practice

1. Plot given ordered pairs. Coordinates should include mixed numbers, positive and negative integers, and rational numbers that include positive and negative square roots.

2. Find, then plot, several ordered pairs using an equation with two variables (above). Connect the points. The straight line (the *graph of the equation*) indicates an endless list of solutions. Because the graph is a straight line, the equation is a *linear equation.*

3. Graph two or three linear equations on the same coordinate plane. Label any points of intersection.

4. Find and graph coordinates for a system and find the solution of the system.

5. Given a line graph, identify a few ordered pairs. (Choose points on the line and determine the coordinates.)

7-8 Objective: Solve and graph inequalities.

Review   The term equation as equal numbers or quantities. $16 = 4 \times 4$

An **inequality** refers to a comparison of number expressions or quantities that are not equal. (E.g., $2 < 3$, and $6 > 4$.)

Students have had experience comparing numbers and using symbols for less than and greater than. Now they will focus on inequalities using variables.

Describing a number

The number is greater than 4 but less than 6 would be written $4 < n < 6$ (any letter may be used). The sum of some number t plus 10 is greater than 20 would be written $t + 10 > 20$.

Solving inequalities

Use inverse operations (addition and subtraction; multiplication and division) as practiced in solving equations. Students are now aware of decimals and fractions as numbers, and should realize that it would not be possible to list all possible solutions to many inequalities.

For $0 < y < 2$, y could be many more possibilities than 1 unless y is defined as a whole number.   If students have difficulty understanding this, have them label points on a number line for decimals or fractions between zero and one.

$n + 12 > 31$	$r - 65 < 10$	$t \times 4 > 12$	$m \div 6 < 120$
$n + 12 - 12 > 31 - 12$	$r - 65 + 65 < 10 + 65$	$t \times 4 \div 4 > 12 \div 4$	$m \div 6 \times 6 < 120 \times 6$
$n > 19$	$r < 75$	$t > 3$	$m < 720$

The solution for an inequality can be graphed on a real number line. Place an empty circle as the starting point and an arrow in the appropriate direction. $t > 3$ would be illustrated with an empty circle on the mark for 3 and a line drawn (an arrow) on top of the number line to the right. The arrow indicates that the possible solutions continue in that direction. For inequalities of greater than *or equal to* $\geq$, or less than *or equal to* $\leq$, use a solid circle at the starting point.

Practice

1. Solve inequalities.

2. Graph solutions of inequalities on a real number line.

7-8 OBJECTIVE: **Simplify expressions.**

The variables and numbers in an expression are called terms. Like terms have the same variable raised to the same power. In the expression 5x + 2x there are two like terms. In the expression 5x² + 2x there are no like terms.

The *coefficient* of a variable is the number in front of it which indicates multiplication. In the expression 9a, 9 is the coefficient of a. It means 9 times a.

To simplify an expression, combine the coefficients of like terms until only unlike terms remain.

$$13x + 4x = (13 + 4)x = 17x \qquad 8x - 12x = (8 - 12)x = -4x$$

$$3x + 2y - 3y = 3x + (2-3)y = 3x + (-1)y = 3x - y$$

Practice simplifying a variety of expressions before solving equations that include like terms.

TOPIC: # MONEY

- Use consumer math materials to apply skills in using percents.
- Solve problems involving tax, simple interest, salary, commission, unit rates, sales discounts, (decrease in price), markups (increase in price), and budgets.
- Students should use formulas to solve problems whenever possible.

A pair of sneakers normally sells for $42.00 but is 20% off.

Discount = 20% of $42
          0.20 x $42 = $8.40 off
          $42 - $8.40 = $33.60 sales price

Salesmen often make their income based on commissions. Commissions are often a percentage of the sales price of a product or service. A real estate salesman may earn 7% of the $15,000 price paid for land he sells for someone else. (He acts as a broker.) To find the commission, find the percent of a number, (7% of $15,000).

Amount of commission = commission rate x sales

The salesman's income could be found with a formula. Income = Commission or Income = commission rate x sales. If the salesman receives a base salary plus a commission on sales, the formula would be Income = Salary + Commission.

Budgets involve percents in assigning a portion of income to various expenses. Have students find the percent an amount represents, and the amount when given the percent. Circle graphs are often used to illustrate budgets.

Businesses have expenses that must be paid from the income. What remains is the profit. Have students solve business problems to find profit, income, or expenses using a formula.

Profit = Income - Expenses

TOPIC: # TIME

Review   Find elapsed time by writing a subtraction problem. Rename as needed. *(Refer to pages 189-190.)*

Friends went shopping at 11:15 A.M. and returned home at 4:30 P.M.
Add 12 hours to 4:30 since it is after noon, then subtract.

$$
\begin{array}{r}
16 \text{ h } 30 \text{ min} \\
- \underline{11 \text{ h } 15 \text{ min}} \\
5 \text{ h } 15 \text{ min}
\end{array}
$$

TOPIC: # GEOMETRY

Review   Definitions of line, line segment, ray, angle, perpendicular and parallel lines *(pages 123, 191, 193)*.

The **midpoint** of a line segment divides it into two equal parts.

Define plane as a set of points on a flat surface that extends without end. Planes that cross each other are called intersecting planes. **Construct geometric figures, perpendicular lines, and angles using a compass and straightedge. Bisect angles using a compass and straightedge.**

Angles
Continue practice finding the measure of angles using a protractor.

Students should be able to measure angles with a protractor and identify the angle as obtuse, right, or acute. A straight line has an angle of 180° which is called a straight angle. They should also identify angles as congruent or not *(page 125)*.

Given a triangle with the degrees of each angle, the student should be able to identify the triangle as acute, right, or obtuse. (Review the sum of angles in a triangle is 180°.)

Introduce angle relationships.

Two angles are **complementary** angles if the sum of their measures is 90°
Two angles are **supplementary** angles if the sum of their measures is 180°
Angles are **adjacent** if they have a common vertex and a common side between them.

When two parallel lines are crossed by a third line (a **transversal**), several pairs of congruent angles are formed: **alternate interior angles** (1 and 2), **corresponding angles** (3 and 4), and **alternate exterior angles** (4 and 5).

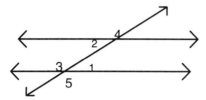

The sum of the angles in a triangle = 180°
The sum of the angles of a polygon can be found using a formula. Sum = (n - 2)180°
n = number of sides

Practice

1. Have students identify the different types of angles.

2. Have students find the value of one angle of a figure when other angles are labeled. (They should use the formula to find the sum, then add known angles and subtract that sum from the total to find the measure of the unknown angle.)

3. Students should construct congruent angles using a compass and straightedge.

4. Students should bisect angles using a straightedge and compass.

Shapes (plane figures)

Review   *(Refer to pages 193-195 as needed.)*
- Classification of polygons and quadrilaterals according to properties.
- Finding lines of symmetry in figures and identifying figures as having no line of symmetry.
- Slides, flips, and turns of figures.

Introduce the geometric terms. A slide is a **translation**, a flip is a **reflection**, and a turn is a **rotation**. All of these moves are called **transformations**. Students should identify transformations of shapes on a coordinate plan using the geometric terms.

Review the definition of **congruent** *(page125)*. Have students identify congruent lines, angles, and figures using symbols for line segments and angles. The symbol used for congruent is ≅. Triangles are identified by a triangle followed by the letters of each vertex.

lines	angles	triangles
$\overline{AB} \cong \overline{CD}$	$\angle A \cong \angle B$	$\triangle ABC \cong \triangle CDE$

Continue to practice finding perimeter and area of squares, rectangles, parallelograms, triangles, trapezoids, and circles using formulas. Tangrams can be used to show the relationships among triangles, squares and parallelograms by using the pieces to create different pictures. (Tangrams are available from several companies listed in *Supplies*, pages 13-14.)

Triangles

Review   Classification of triangles—right, acute, obtuse, equilateral, isosceles, scalene.

Have students identify a triangle as acute, right, or obtuse according to the measures of angles.

Identify and determine measures of corresponding sides of similar triangles.

Congruent angles of **similar** (same shape, not necessarily same size) triangles should be marked. Similar triangles have corresponding angles which are congruent and corresponding sides which are in proportion. <u>Find the unknown length of a side of one triangle by writing a proportion.</u>

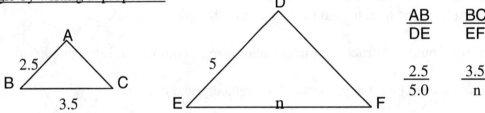

Students have described some sides of triangles as equal in length. These lines are *congruent*.

Students should identify illustrations of congruent triangles and polygons which use symbols to mark congruent sides. Congruent angles may be marked with curved lines, or labeled with the degrees of measurement. **Two congruent polygons have corresponding sides and corresponding angles that are congruent.** Students may use the rules for identifying congruent triangles. Have them identify congruent polygons.

$$\overline{AC} \cong \overline{DF}$$

$$\overline{BC} \cong \overline{EF}$$

$$\overline{AB} \cong \overline{ED}$$

Rules for congruent triangles

Side-Angle-Side (SAS)
Two sides and the angle formed by those two sides of one triangle are congruent to the corresponding sides and angle of another triangle.

Side-Side-Side (SSS)
Three sides of one triangle are congruent to the 3 sides of another triangle.

Angle-Side-Angle (ASA)
Two angles and the side between them of one triangle are congruent to the corresponding angles and side of another triangle.

Tangent Ratios

Tangent ratios are included in a study of triangles. Each side of a right triangle has a name. The two sides that form the right angle are **legs**. One leg is the **adjacent side**, the other is the **opposite side.** The third side of the triangle, opposite the right angle, is called the **hypotenuse.**

*The **tangent** of an angle for a **right triangle** is the ratio of the length of the opposite side to the length of the adjacent side. If two angles are congruent, their tangents will be equal.*

*The **sine** of an angle for a right triangle is the ratio of the length of the opposite side to the length of the hypotenuse. If two angles are congruent, their sines are equal.*

*The **cosine** of an angle of a right triangle is the ratio of the length of the adjacent side to the length of the hypotenuse. If two angles are congruent, their cosines are equal.*

Provide materials with illustrations, tables, and practice problems for students to write tangent, sine, and cosine ratios.

Pythagorean Theorem

Review the sum of the angles of a triangle is 180°.
In a right triangle the side opposite the right angle is called the hypotenuse. A Greek mathematician named Pythagoras proved a property called the Pythagorean Theorem which states that in a right triangle the square of the length of the hypotenuse is equal to the sum of the squares of the lengths of the other two sides (the legs). It is written as $c^2 = a^2 + b^2$ (a and b represent legs, c represents the hypotenuse).

In any right triangle with the other angles measuring 30° and 60°, the length of the side opposite the 30° angle is ½ the length of the hypotenuse.

In an isosceles right triangle, the two legs are equal in length. The measures of the angles opposite the legs are 45° each.

Practice

1. If you know the lengths of the sides of a triangle, use the Pythagorean formula to determine whether or not it is a right triangle. (Does the formula work with the information given?)

After practice with square roots solve the types of problems below.

2. Given the length of the legs, find the hypotenuse of right triangles.

3. Given the length of the hypotenuse and one leg, find the length of the other leg.

4. Given a right triangle with 60° and 30° as the measure of the other two angles, and the length of the shorter leg, find the length of the longer leg.

5. Given the length of the shorter leg of a 30°- 60° right triangle, find the length of the longer leg.

6. Given the length of one leg, find the hypotenuse of an isosceles right triangle.

Solids (space figures)

Review   Classification of various prisms, and pyramids, cones, cylinders, and spheres according to faces, vertices, and edges *(pages 191-193).*

Cross Sections of Solids

Slice a solid (e.g., cut an orange—a *sphere*—in half). The new face is the cross section. Students should be aware of the shape of that face when a variety of solids are cut vertically or horizontally. Students should be able to identify the shape of a cross section of a solid when shown an illustration of the figure with a plane slicing it.

SURFACE AREA

The surface area is the sum of the area of each face and base. Finding surface area of solids involves finding the area of squares, triangles, rectangles, and circles. Review any forgotten formulas. *(Refer to pages 198, 201, and 204 as needed.)*

Cylinder   The surface of a cylinder can be thought of as a tube (lateral area) with a circle (base) at each end. If the tube were cut top to bottom and then flattened, it would form a rectangle whose width would be the same as the circumference of one base ($2\pi r$). To find the rectangle's area we multiply the width times the height of the cylinder: $2\pi rh$. The two circles each have an area πr^2, so $2\pi r^2$ equals both of their areas. The lateral area plus 2 times the area of a base, then, would be the total surface area (S): $S = 2\pi rh + 2\pi r^2$

VOLUME

Find the volume of cones and pyramids.
If a pyramid is filled with water and the water is poured into a prism of the same height and with a congruent base, the prism would be one third full. (Use models)

If a cone is filled with water and the water poured into a cylinder with a congruent base and the same height, the cylinder will be one third full.

Volume of a pyramid or cone: $V = \frac{1}{3}Bh$ (B = area of the base)

Find the volume of prisms.
Volume (V) = Area of base (B) x height (h) **V = Bh**

Find the volume of cylinders.
V = Bh <u>The base is a circle.</u> Use the formula for finding the area of a circle to find the area of the base, then multiply that times the height of the cylinder.

TOPIC: # MEASUREMENT

7-8 OBJECTIVE: **Identify precision in measurement.**

All measurements are approximations. How exact, or precise, a measurement is depends on the unit used. The smaller the unit, the closer it is to the exact amount. Objects are measured "to the nearest" something and, therefore, have a range of error. When a student measures the length of a pencil to the nearest centimeter, he decides if the length is closer to one number or the other. The range of error is 0.5 cm either way. The pencil measures 13 cm ± 0.5 cm. That is, its actual length is somewhere between 12.5 cm and 13.5 cm. This **half unit** of allowance more and less than the measurement is called the **greatest possible error (GPE)** of the measurement. It is read as *twelve centimeters plus or minus five-tenths centimeters.*

To the nearest liter, a measurement of 6 liters would have a GPE of 0.5 liters and the capacity would be written 6 ± 0.5 L. The minimum amount would be 5.5 liters, and the maximum amount would be 6.5 liters.

Practice

1. Determine the GPE for a variety of measurements and units (units of length, weight, capacity).

2. Choose the more precise measurement when given a choice.
   302 mL or 0.5 L   mL is the smaller unit and more precise.

7-8 OBJECTIVE: **Convert metric units of measurement.**

Review conversion by multiplication and division. *(Refer to pages 204-205 as needed.)* At this level, students should understand the shortcut of moving the decimal point to convert units mentally. Practice is often necessary to reinforce the direction to move the decimal more than the number of places.

The exponent or number of zeros in the power of ten tells how many places to move the decimal. Multiplication indicates the decimal moves right. Division indicates the decimal moves left. Multiply when converting from a greater unit to a lesser unit. Divide when converting from a lesser unit to a greater unit.

A number times 100 or 10² would move the decimal two places to the right.
A number divided by 100 would move the decimal two places to the left.

Convert 1 liter to milliliters: 1 x 1,000 = 1,000 mL (1,000 mL to 1 L)

Practice converting units within a system.
4 kL = *40* hL   9,000 L = *900* daL = *90* hL = *9* kL
2 hg = *20* dag   3,000 cg = *300* dg = *30* g

Add and subtract units within a system, renaming as needed.   45 yd 20 in → 44 yd 56 in
                                                              − 6 yd 23 in   − 6 yd 23 in

7-8 OBJECTIVE: **Solve problems involving measurements.**

1. Add and subtract with units of measurement, renaming as needed. Answers should be in simplest terms.
2. Find the difference in temperatures.
3. Find perimeter, area, and volume of geometric figures using formulas.
4. Use the formula distance = rate x time.
5. Use scale drawings as a source of information for measurement problems.
    Include finding distance using scales on maps.
6. Identify cities by longitude and latitude coordinates on a map.